HOW TO ACHIEVE ANY GOAL AND TRANSFORM YOUR LIFE

OLLIE CAMPBELL

Chichester, England

First published in 2019 by
Lotus Publishing
Apple Tree Cottage, Inlands Road, Nutbourne, Chichester, PO18 8RJ

Text Design Medlar Publishing Solutions Pvt Ltd., India
Cover Design Alissa Dinallo
Printed and Bound in the UK by Clays Limited, Bungay

British Library Cataloging-in-Publication Data
A CIP record for this book is available from the British Library
ISBN 978 1 913088 01 9

DEDICATION

This book is dedicated to my wife, Emily, without whom none of what I get to do would be possible, and to my two children, Oscar and Lillie, from whom all my motivation stems.

CONTENTS

ACKNOWLEDGEMENTS

I would like to thank:

AJ Roberts, who was the first person to make me realise that business can be fun and an expression of self, and who inspired me to want more. He made me aware of the fact that I had put a limit on the glass ceiling for myself – but one that was I was capable of smashing.

The late Charles Poliquin, for influencing my career more than any other strength coach. He made me realise that this was a career rather than a stepping stone. One of his many philosophies that stuck with me was 'learn more, to earn more'. But not only that, he was a firm believer that learning and educating oneself were essential in order to progress.

Derek Woodske, **Andre Benoit** and **John Connor** for teaching a training course which gave me hope in the industry, set high standards of professionalism and furnished me with the tools to succeed.

Ben Bergeron for his podcast Chasing Excellence, which has had a big influence on many of my morning rambles. He describes and explains mindset in a way that the average human can relate to, and makes them feel that they can achieve excellence.

Bedros Keuilian for his podcast with **Craig Ballantyne**, and the book *Man-Up*. These guys have inspired me to believe that there is no limit to business progress and happiness, and I highly recommend seeking out their information.

Sam Dancer for his mindset of love and spreading happiness. If you want to witness a giant of a man lift heavy things while being one of the nicest humans on the planet, look no further.

My parents, without whom I obviously wouldn't hold the values I do. Hard work, persistence, love and family – these are the things that have carried over from my childhood.

Then there are all the clients I have trained and learned from. Every problem we've solved together, every tear they have shed, and all the effort they have put in have given me the opportunity to try to help them and the next person down the line. They have made the writing of this book possible... they have made owning a gym a reality.

INTRO

I have ADHD. I am not an intellect. I was never given any chance as an academic at school.

If you had said there was one thing I would not have had the patience or ability to do, it would have been to write a book.

I was put down, I was ridiculed, I was told I couldn't.

As a problem solver and as a person who cannot be around negativity, I developed a way whereby I could defy the odds. I have an ability to seek out positivity. I am a normal person... physically I am by no means blessed but I work hard and above all else I am consistent. This is a learnt trait – it's not something I was born with, it's been crafted.

I have fond memories of my grandfather (Gar Gar) teaching me his wisdom of effort and consistency. I remember the day like it was yesterday, lying on his and my nanna's bedroom floor and he said this week do one press-up a day, next week two, the week after three. That was my first exposure to consistency. The second was a trip back to school, driving across the chalk valleys of Wiltshire in his white Golf. The simple idea that in whatever you do, give an extra 5%, the 'extra percentage effort'. That was probably my first memory of self-improvement. He probably didn't know at the time that these lessons would stay with me for my entire life. They somewhat shaped my belief that I was the only person who could be the 'master of my fate and the captain of my soul' (to steal a quote from William Ernest Henry).

This book, however, all started when I realised that I wasted so much time on the way to and from work – 30 mins of dead time. So, I thought to myself, how could I make use of that time? How could I use it to my advantage? I started to listen to podcasts about fitness and health, nutrition and wellness. I had access to some of the best people in the world on my phone. This wonderful device brought the world's experts to me.

One of the most influential podcasts I listened to talked of getting your 10,000 steps a day. I bought a Fitbit and tracked my steps.

This led me to take a morning walk each day, during which I could extend my learning. Before I knew it, I was doing an hour of learning a day.

I've always wanted to defy the odds and write a book. So, I came up with the concept of the morning rambles. I would commit to writing a book. In small daily chunks, I'd listen to a concept, a philosophy, and then translate it into a useable action for the general public. You see, experts talk to other experts. They forget that most of us don't understand them... they need to be translated. I'm a simple person – I understand the technical and the thought process, but sometimes you just want to see it in plain English. Thus began the morning rambles of a fitness fanatic. Out of these, the Build the Chain concept was born. A concept so simple, yet more powerful than anything I've experienced. A way of daily showing up and becoming a better human – a better version of yourself, a better father, mother, friend, athlete, dog owner... Whatever goal you have, it's an ongoing process, and what this does is keep you true to your focus – you turn up daily, you read and you take action.

That is the Build the Chain way. I wrote this book entirely on my iPhone, at 5.30 in the morning while everyone else slept. I wrote my book, I built the chain, I defied the odds and I proved I am capable of whatever I want to be. I even wrote this intro on my phone, that little iPhone 8, wandering through a countryside walk surrounded by nature, my dog Chase running in front of me, cows to the left (retired Dexter cattle), and overgrown paths of nettles stinging my legs. I committed to writing a book... I didn't know what. Originally it was going to be fitness based but it turned into much, much more, while still using fitness as a guide, as it's the industry I've dedicated over 10 years of my life to.

Now the time has come to Build the Chain...

#buildthechain

How to Build the Chain

It's all about knowing what you want to achieve and then why you want to achieve it. You can Build the Chain without knowing your 'why', but I've seen over the last 10 or so years that those who can identify their 'why', firstly get there faster and secondly stay there. It seems a bit airy-fairy, and it may seem a bit 'therapy'-like, but you're here reading this because you want to change something... so settle down and follow the goal-setting guidelines. Have an explore, if you will, into your mind and really start to ask some hard questions. If you aren't ready for that, that's fine, you'll still be taking action towards your goal... and, at some point, you may be ready. Action is most important though.

Build the Chain and this first edition is all about creating a much bigger influence. There will be training books, nutrition books and cooking books all written in the same format as this one. Daily actions towards the goals. The mission is to CHANGE lives. How many, not sure... as many as possible really. The more content I can create, the more potential there is for change. Ultimately, it will end up with a network allowing me to change childhood obesity, change the way fitness is delivered to children, and change the gym dynamic to one of quality of movement, health and performance for anyone who will listen. This will involve setting personal records to show that setting a target and delivering on it is as simple as daily actions delivered. Turn up daily and take those actions, and you and I as normal people can do extraordinary things that most people don't believe we can do. Defy the odds, achieve any goal and transform your life.

So how do we go about setting our goals and what's the process? How do we move from thinking about it to actually achieving it?

Firstly, we need to look at goal setting in general and break a few things down.

THE DIFFERENT TYPES OF GOAL SETTING

Self-setting of goals takes place when you set the goals for yourself. These, I believe, are the ticket to self-happiness and self-growth. Creating your own goals often leads to ownership of the goal. We can still use people around us to more clearly define the goals and help us in exploring the options, but the origins come from ourselves and what they mean to us.

Outcome goals highlight a specific desired result, such as losing 7kg, getting down to 10% body fat (which usually in most cases would accentuate the abs), or even writing a book. It doesn't appear that outcome-based goals alone are ever the best answer... they tend to be future based without action. However, they can be effective in helping define a target to aim for.

Process goals (the base of Build the Chain) are strategies that people may use to achieve a goal. For us, this is the most powerful way of achieving our dreams. Build the Chain is built on applying these principles – daily actionable and accountable goals. Put simply, if I did this on a daily basis, will it take me closer to my goal? It's the key to ticking off, day by day, moving in the right direction.

Short-term goals are mini milestones along the way... they are goals that are set for the near future. Depending on the outcome goal, you can set short-term goals weekly, monthly or quarterly to build 'check-points' that will allow you to see your progress towards the main goal, which you wrote down as your long-term outcome goal. Short-term goals have been found to be more motivating than long-term goals, because you feel yourself ticking off the daily actions, and they can be especially useful for beginners to enjoy early success.

The point of goal setting is to start the process of breaking your goal down to make it achievable and visible. The more clearly defined each part is, the more you are going to be able to draw motivation from your actions. You will begin to find out the person you need to be in order to achieve these goals (after all, the only difference between the person you are now and the person you want to become is that the future you already does all the daily actions that the current you identifies). You will know exactly how you are going to achieve the goals through the steps that you will take.

GOAL SETTING EXERCISE

When starting a combination of all of the above, goal definition is paramount to your success. Here's a process you could use, but be willing to deviate from the process when you need to... if you identify a certain type of goal that leads to greater buy-in, use it.

1. Long-term Goal

Start out with the outcome goal, which should also be a long-term goal. It's much better if this is specific rather than vague. Most people have heard of the acronym SMART:

S-Specific
M-Measurable
A-Achievable
R-Realistic
T-Time

As an example, try to 'lose 7kg' rather than 'get leaner' by nine months' time. This will likely motivate you more and help guide your compass. It gives you the ability to break it down further too, which will be shown in the next step.

It's also important to ask yourself why you want to accomplish this goal. We're much more likely to persevere through the tough times if we are clear about the reasoning of our goals. Real-life examples include: I want to lose 20kg so I feel more confident ... so that I can ask a girl out, get married and have children. I don't want to be defined as the 'jolly fat guy'. That is a real story and actually happened!

If you don't have a long-term goal, ask yourself why you're interested in improving your nutrition, fitness, health or physical appearance in the first place. It's often a hard question to ask yourself, but if you don't, you're leaving valuable motivation on the table.

2. Short-term Goal

Next in the series is to identify short-term goals that are challenging but doable. I like to ask: what is the single thing that I could do right now that will move the needle the furthest? The goal (no pun intended) with these is to build a sense of success immediately, something to aim for in the now... a quick focal point along the way. In the example above of losing 7kg in nine months, the short-term goals might be: lose 3kg by month three, 3kg by month six, and 1kg by month nine. In other words, the long-term goal is broken down into shorter-term manageable 'projects'.

3. Process or #buildthechain

This is where you begin your Build the Chain journey. This is where the magic happens and we start to hold accountability for our actions and how much we truly want a particular goal. Once you've identified the long-term and short-term goals, it's time to break them down. In other words, what is the process or strategy for getting there? What habits do you need to adopt? This is where having a coach can help. I call them the 'accountability coach'. No one has trouble saying 'I want to lose 7kg', or 'I want to stop eating junk' or 'I want to write a book'. What people need help with is identifying the strategies for actually achieving those things. This is where, in my body transformation groups, we spend the majority of the time operating ... checking off those daily actions.

When deciding to write this book, I realised early on that I simply could not sit down and write it... I needed to find another way. I knew I wanted to write it but needed a way to keep myself accountable. I needed a way of saying that in six months' time

I would have the content written for a book. I came up with the following process goals that I thought would give me the best possible chance to write a book:

- Every day, walk for 30 mins.
- Every day, listen to a podcast on a subject that inspires me or from a person who inspires me.
- Every day, write about that subject I had listened to in health, fitness, self-improvement.

Doing these actions meant that I would achieve my goal of writing enough content for a book in six months.

All I had to do was turn up daily, listen and write. The morning ramblings were born.

Building the Chain was a way of ticking this off daily. I would tick off the days I did go out and write – a simple X on the day. Soon enough, there was a chain of Xs so long I didn't want to break the chain. I could see my goal materialising simply by turning up and doing it. Just 14 days in and I had 14 different interesting posts. About what? Well, what I would do is listen to a person far more knowledgeable than myself, someone at the top of their field... for most it is often complex, and too inaccessible to the general population. People don't always understand the top in the field. So, I tried to make the material more accessible... simpler... easier to understand. If I could explain it in a way I could understand, then hopefully others would and could benefit from these gurus' teachings. Quite often as well, people would never even know that these gurus exist. I'm trying to help both types of people out... trying to spread the word of these gurus, but in a way that people can immediately understand and then seek out these people for themselves.

Building a chain link by link gave me a visual and metaphorical way to 'see' my progress towards my goal, day by day. I could see that goal getting closer because of my actions. It was simple. I'd broken down something enormous into a daily task, much like in fitness by turning up to the gym to get fitter, or in eating healthily simply by the act of starting the day with a good breakfast. I realised during this process that Building the Chain could be applied to ANY goal, whether it be money, business, fitness, nutrition or weight loss related... literally any goal whereby daily action is needed.

4. Assess and Reassess

Continually assessing your path is another key determinant of greatness. Reflection Friday has been a weekly chain builder for me – reflecting on the processes that have gone well and those that have needed work. Look for two things:

1. The progress that you've made towards your goal. Whatever the goal, there are indicator markers along the way that will allow you to track your progress. For weight loss or a body transformation, the progress could be indicated by the scales, mirror, energy, mood, sleep, etc. Looking at the progress that you've made can keep you positive and confident in your ability to succeed. RECORD that feeling!

2. Breakdowns in strategy or ways that you see you can be EVEN better. After you've celebrated something that you're doing well, then find something that you can improve on... there's always something that could have made your progress even better. In this step, be careful not to discount the thing that you're doing well when finding ways to improve. Three questions that can help you identify the cause of the breakdowns are:

    i.   What, outside of your control, has made things difficult this week to achieve your daily actions? (For example, kids waking up in the middle of the night, leading to decreased sleep time.)

    ii. What habits are causing you difficulty in achieving your daily actions? (For example, watching a series on TV that finishes dead on the time that you are meant to be turning the lights out.)

    iii. Are there other people making it difficult for you to achieve your goals? This is always a tricky one, as it often requires awkward conversations with friends, a spouse, etc. (For example, friends offering nights out, or a spouse cooking that extra portion.)

Again, this is where having a coach to talk to, strategise and assist you will help massively. Being able to talk through with someone whose focus is your goal will enable you to handle some difficult conversations.

5. Goal Completion or Incompletion

One of two things will always happen in regard to your goals. Either you will complete them or you won't. There is no halfway, almost, or maybes. Its finite! When put this way, it's almost as finite as life and death. It's important to not gloss over that fact, as many people get distracted from, or forget to complete, their goals.

If the goal is completed, first CELEBRATE with something positive: a gift or a trip – something that is a positive reinforcement of your accomplishment. Then the time comes to set a new challenging goal, following the same process as before. This can simply be the same goal but with a bigger outcome (e.g. lose 14kg instead of 7kg), or it could be a completely different goal altogether – make it progressive – make it a continuation and subject to the previous goal. I like to point out here that a lot of people set new goals before they achieve the current one... we have all done it. A great book for concentrating on the task in hand is 'The One Thing'. It's based on business practices, but the principle of concentrating on one thing until its completion is paramount to the feeling of success and motivation.

If you don't meet your goal, then simply reassess and work out why. You can try to identify objectively what prevented you from meeting the goal. Again, having a coach in your corner here can help you to identify more clearly. It is difficult to have that level of clarity in your own life. More importantly, this is a great time to set new goals and build the motivation. You will be able to make better ones based on previous experience. Follow the same process as before. Get that coach involved in the process – they are there not to GET you your goal but to HELP you get to the goal. (As a coach, if I understand the goal-setting process, it allows me to keep you accountable that much better.) The coach give you the tools and support you and guide you, but ultimately YOU get to achieve it.

We call it... Building the Chain

THE MORNING RAMBLINGS

TUESDAY

January 2: Ramblings 2018 is a GO!!!

When it gets hard, who you gonna call? Most people by now have some form of goal... you've got it mapped out. The goals are ambitious, and this year is going to be different. Chances are you have thought about, or been trying to achieve, that goal for a while. But, truthfully, I have seen lots of people express goals and not follow through than I have committed and achieved... goals are hard to achieve. The question is... what do you have to put in place when the going gets HARD? When motivation is high and it's a new thing, it's easy. But what about in 22 days' time at that first moment when you're cold, feeling fed up, work is stressful, kids are playing up and you've got to make a decision for your supper AND book onto your CrossFit class in the morning? What then? Have you planned for that? Chances are you haven't. Because the current situation that motivated you, hasn't considered the hard times yet! So, let's get PROACTIVE rather than REACTIVE.

Here's a great way to stay on the right track:

- Buy either a wall or book of a whole calendar year. Have your goals written out above it and stick it up on the wall.
- Each day you do the processes through which you achieve your goals, put a BIG green X through the day. Right now, it should be easy to hit those Xs. Your aim is to NOT BREAK THE HABIT CHAIN!

The habit chain is a new OC concept. If I was a marketing genius, I'd probably sell it online as a book and make millions. I guarantee that once you see 10 days in a row of big GREEN Xs, you're going to think twice about unbooking that class or choosing a takeaway over your nutrition plan... Ask yourself:

DO YOU REALLY WANT TO BREAK THE HABIT CHAIN? It's powerful because it hands YOU the CHOICE to make or break your goal in a visual and easy to see way!

'But Ollie, what happens if I do succumb and the chain is broken?' Simple. You write down the number of days you did manage to chain together (e.g. the days you went to class)... Then, you call or message your coach and you identify why you broke the chain... Then, you, here's the important part: MOVE ON and try to better the chain... beat your last run.

In fact, this is such a good idea that I'm going to add it to our private P6 Forum and use it with all my clients...

Go out and buy a wall chart and let's see who can have the longest habit chain...

Ramblings out! Your chain has started!

Email me at... Ollie@ocfitness.co.uk so I can congratulate you on starting the chain.

WEDNESDAY

January 3

The transformation conundrum, goals and Building the Chain! Is it wrong to want to be less fat? Is it wrong to want to look better (in your own eyes)? Is it wrong to want to look the best you can be? Do you know what that is?

Should you go for 'Strong is the new sexy'? What is strong? Should you just aim to get stronger and then be comfortable with how your body looks when you're stronger? What if you get bulky? What if you don't want to look like this or like that?

It's round about this time of the year that people commit to their goals, or at least attempt to, but with so many options out there, what is the right goal for you? So many people bash everyone else's goals, probably because they are insecure in their own goals, that it's virtually impossible to choose a goal without someone giving their opinion on your perceived endpoint.

Here's the thing: it's YOUR goal – go after what YOU want to achieve. If you want to look a certain way, train and eat towards that goal. If you want to be strong and athletic looking, then train for it. My goal has always been to train to look like a superhero. Never got there, lol. However, this year the emphasis will shift

PRIORITY 6 PHILOSOPHY

BUILD THE HABIT CHAIN
SEEK HELP
WHEN YOU NEED IT!

Sp Adobe Spark

to look AND perform like a superhero as I transition back into a sport. The first part hasn't fully gone to plan, as I've got to navigate around a knee injury, so will be concentrating on building upper body strength and structural balance. Posterior chain work will be done, hopefully, via taking out the muscles below the glutes ... What I'm getting at is that throughout the year, you are going to encounter difficulties and obstacles that will make your goal seem harder, further away, unachievable. There will be moments when you doubt yourself. That is the time for you to look at yourself in the mirror and remind yourself of why you started, and for you to look at the habit chain you have built and ask, do you want to break it?

There is always something you can do to further yourself towards your goal. The sport I'm going to play requires a lot of running short intervals... I can't run currently and may not be able to for a good while. Some would let this put them off training entirely, but I'm lucky that I have the knowledge and friends in the training world to help me put myself in the best place possible for when I CAN use my legs again. SEEK OUT HELP! If you have an injury and think you can't train, reach out to a professional. They are wanting to help you, it's their mission!

THURSDAY

January 4

S hort ramblings cos it's peeing with rain. And you can't type in the rain on a mobile phone!

> Turn up daily
> Enjoy it daily
> Understand it doesn't happen overnight
> Every night cross off the box
> Be grateful for all you have and all you can BECOME
> Go do it – it's your choice

#alwaysimprovealwaysevolvenevergiveup
#buildthechain

FRIDAY

January 5

S orry, it's a long one! But hopefully, someone out there changes course because of it!

Walking through the door... is hard.

The only things in life we have control over are our choices and reactions.

Walking through the door and starting your journey is a CHOICE.

One that you may or may not be ready to make. But at this present moment, that is your choice.

Let's talk about why you are not ready...

Are you scared? It's a realistic and valuable fear to start on something that will ultimately change the course of your life. It involves being uncomfortable, where now you may look at yourself and feel you are worth more but at least you're used to the

current you. It doesn't take effort to maintain the current version of yourself – it's routine.

> Change is HARD!
> Quite often, people fail. NO ONE LIKES TO FAIL!
> So, what can we do about it?
> We can educate.

Five areas where you could implement EASY changes to help you make the decision to walk through the door:

1. Training.
You perceive this as a hard one. In fact, it's going to end up the easy one. Eventually, it's the one you enjoy, it's the one you wish you had started earlier. You think it's going to be too hard, but

when you get there, you realise the coaches have altered the workouts (as they do for everyone) to suit your ability, and you have been through the process of learning what each movement is and you can do them. In the meantime, know this: if you think you need to get fit before coming, you are missing the point of what we, as coaches, do. We get you to that stage and then help you move on further than you ever imagined, to the stage of ENJOYMENT!

2. Nutrition (keep your eyes peeled for Feb 2018).
The simpler it is, in terms of principles, the better it works. Do you need the XYZ diet? No, you need to assess your goal and then feed yourself according to that goal CONSISTENTLY. Is it easy? Well, actually, it is when the penny drops and you realise that you are not an anomaly. Our fundamental principles work for ANYONE, and the fine tuning comes when you have learnt the phases we go through. There are four phases to our nutritional programming, but most people never need to go further than phase three.

3. Recovery. The downtime.
What do you need to be doing outside of the training and nutrition window? For most, just staying active and moving is about it. Athletes and those going to the extreme need more recovery tactics. For the general population: chill out, stress less. Things like massage, therapy and mental recovery are all key to a better you.

4. Sleep.
Ah, the missing link to so many people's journeys. I've trained many a doctor or night shift worker, and the thing that affects their results more than anything is their sleep. It's not impossible, but it takes effort. For parents and commuters, you need to maximise the hours in bed. That means building a solid routine. I cannot stress enough the importance of sleep. Take it from someone who is the parent of a 6-week-old and who is meticulous in tracking data. When the only change is a sleep pattern and you see the results and stats shift, it's easy to see the importance.

5. Lastly, the mindset.
The rabbit hole – the most powerful and controllable thing that everyone perceives they have no control over. I've listened to and read an amazing amount of educational material on this subject. I've seen the powerful impact it can have. It's one that you have to work on daily, but the biggest change comes when you finally realise that the decisions you make, the choices and your reaction are in fact owned by you.

A really simple example:

> Stuck in traffic.
> Two choices.

First choice: get freaking angry. It gets you nowhere faster, it puts you in a crap mood, it affects your day because YOU CHOSE to be angry.

Another choice: ring the appointment and tell them you are stuck in traffic.

Now use the time. For me, it's a chance to learn something: a podcast, an audiobook. I make the choice to make it a positive choice.

The result: you get there at the same time, BUT less stress learnt and therefore professed yourself happier and closer to your goal of a better version of you.

Very simple example, but a very clear message that the CHOICE IS YOURS.

That's it for the ramblings this week. Last year, I did Saturdays as well. I've dedicated that time to extra sleep or getting my training done so I can spend more family time.

Keep up with your goals, stay in control this weekend. Be a master of your CHOICES and #buildthechain.

Monday

January 8

Monday ramblings and typing! It's not often that the lazy ever get where they want to get. It sounds silly but how often are we lazy? Can be in anything... loads. It often, therefore, spills over into our actual workouts.

Going through the motions, it's a lazy approach to a workout. Not to think about the rep, the set, the technique, the set-up, the FOCUS. After all, we are there at the gym to take our mind off the other shizzle in our lives, so why not take the time to really engage and make sure you a) get the most out of the workout, and b) think about it so much that the rest of your days are left behind.

There are times that we've all done it. We just go to 'get the workout done' so that we can feel righteous that we've done it. How many sessions have you done where perhaps you could have looked out another rep or added 0.5kg to the bar, but at the time you didn't? But reflecting back, there are a few workouts where (even though you're working out and that's amazing and should be applauded) you've been lazy.

What am I getting at? Basically, it's about not squandering the opportunity. We're lucky that we live in a privileged society, one where we get to care about our fitness and health, one where we can make a choice to train our bodies and live our lives to the fullest of our capabilities. Do not waste that chance... fill that time with a workout ethic to be proud of. That starts from the moment you enter, the set-up, the placement of the weights, the self-talk, the technique cues, the bracing, the breathing, the grip, the joint alignment. It's a chain, so any weak links in your concentration or lack of attention to detail and the lift is missed or you could have done more. It comes down to the same phrase you've been using this year: Build the Chain, no weak links, add each link of the chain with purpose, smash each session and love the fact you are able to do it!

This week: continue to build on last week... if you have an UNBROKEN CHAIN, build on it, make it strong and long! If your chain was broken, are you back on it? Have you evaluated why it broke? Reflection is proactive and useful, while negativity is useless and unproductive for a better you!

#buildthechain
Ramblings out

TUESDAY

January 9: Ramblings.

Yesterday I started reading the new Tim Ferris book 'Tribe of Mentors'. He asks all the interviewees a series of 11 questions. Two people in and I'm hooked. I love to read what successful people have to say. It brings my creative mind to the forefront and they make you realise that you should trust the process and believe in yourself. If things go wrong, don't worry… they are meant to, and most of all just enjoy life. At the time when things go wrong, everything seems crap. It is, it's meant to feel that way, but it is that feeling that makes you realise how good things are when they go right!

Right now, hopefully, everything for you is going right in your fitness and health journey of 2018. If it's not, a) why not? and b) how can I help? P6 wasn't ever designed to be a singular entity, one place of doing. We were always meant to branch out, be remote... be accessible to anyone anywhere. That's why we try to spread our advice through social media (the biggest platform to reach the widest audience). Annoyingly, there isn't just one platform (no idea how Snap Chat works properly... I should probably learn).

We've got grand plans in 2018 to branch out even more, into the unknown. They are big goals, scary ones. Much like your goals, there are elements of it that seem unattainable, and I know I'm going to have to work very hard at not falling flat on my face. But work I shall. Effort and consistency bring about opportunities, but if they don't come, at least you have put yourself in the best possible position regardless. Coming back to the concept of Building the Chain. Consistently turning up and ticking off the days. No one will give you the results you want unless you're willing to work hard for them. The rewards come from the process of setting and working towards your goals. The stuff you learn on the way is incredible. Today, I'd highly recommend going out and buying Tim's books. All of them have had a massive influence on my life.

#buildthechain

WEDNESDAY

January 10: Ramblings, ramble, ramble...
This came up in conversation yesterday.

Comparing yourself to Mat Fraser or Katrin Davidsdottir (two of the world's top CrossFit Athletes) is like trying to catch

You are probably not the top 0.1% of the physically gifted.... sorry but you are not Usain Bolt. But what you are is still AWESOME

PRIORITY 6

Adobe Spark

lightning in a glass bottle. You're comparing yourself to the absolute elite. Sometimes you have to accept you are simply not that gifted... you are not Usain Bolt!

You may be stronger than them, but you don't have the engine.

You may have a better engine, but not the lifting skill.

You may have the skills, but don't have the mental fortitude to be a champion.

Stop comparing yourself to the top of the food chain. Instead focus on you and your improvement and be happy!

A lot of people nowadays are getting into CrossFit having seen the elite perform. While they are amazing and to be admired, a lot of people forget they are the creme de la creme. They are superior physical beings. By all means, use them as motivation... you can want to be LIKE them but you cannot BE them.

Instead, focus on YOUR goals and your processes.

Today what is the single most bang for buck thing you could do to help you reach your goal?

I know what mine is in three areas of my life that I have goals:

- Family
- Business
- Health

They are locked in, they are what I need to do to keep the chain unbroken...

Ramblings out... #buildthechain

P.S. I am aware that somewhere out there the future CrossFit Games champion who would blow Fraser out the water may be reading this. They are probably 16 years old with a 130 snatch, a 10-sec 100m time, a 17-min 5km. They have done gymnastics since they could walk and can squat 180 for reps. They are probably 175cm and weigh about 85kg... Follow your dreams, be great!

THURSDAY

January 11

Ramblings for today (I reckon the temp has dropped 10 degrees, so currently my hands are freezing).

Simplicity is often overlooked!

Take nutrition. You know what the first stage of my nutritional advice comes down to (depending on goals, time frame, knowledge, ability)?... keeping it SIMPLE.

TOP TIP: SIMPLICITY IS OVERLOOKED

Sp Adobe Spark

It's the tidy-up stage. It's not exciting, it's not complicated... we don't omit food groups. It's about creating the system, educating, practising, Building the Chain, creating a food list of 'safe' foods, ones that don't trigger binges and cravings.

It's about making sure you know what a vegetable is, it's about knowing where your protein comes from, it's about knowing what a carbohydrate is. It's about creating a base from which to work from. It's asking yourself the questions: can I be consistent and what are the challenges I'm going to face? Nutrition runs deeper than nutrition – it's a source of fun and enjoyment for some but punishment for others. There are times we need to dial it in according to the goal. There are times when the order can bring around massive changes. But there are also times for reflection and intuitive eating, where boundaries do not need to be pushed.

That doesn't mean stuffing your face with lots of foods with no nutritional value. It means going back to basics and re-establishing a comfortable set point from which to work... that good old 80/20 rule. In hard times, when the stresses of life take hold, look at your plate... If you aim for 80% from nutrient-dense whole foods based on single ingredients and 20% from convenience or pre-made foods, you're going to be within touching distance of your goal all year round.

#buildthechain
Ramblings out

FRIDAY

January 12: A shorter Friday ramble?

Are you having fun with it? With everything in life, in order to succeed you have to enjoy it and have fun with it to some degree. Here's an example of someone having fun with a multimillion-dollar company: Elon Musk, CEO of Tesla, the car company. Want to know a difference between Tesla and other electric car companies? As a nod to his favourite band Spinal Tap, you can turn your Tesla sound system up to an '11'. A great example of someone having fun with what they do.

Enjoy the process, have fun with it. In health and fitness nothing happens overnight, but when you Build the Chain and enjoy it (which comes from consistently turning up and improving) with a smile on your face... that's when true excellence appears.

This weekend, the challenge is to sit down and evaluate whether you 'enjoy' it... What is 'it'?... can be anything – fitness, nutri~ job, hobby, tv programmes. Do you enjoy it? If not, CAN it? Would a change in direction help, or is there some help or teach you a way to enjoy it?

Have a great Friday, start planning the weekend and start planning how you're going to keep the chain unbroken. Remember, there is no shame in breaking the chain... it's about having fewer breaks than you would without the method. It's about accountability, it's about learning the triggers, so that in the future you know what, where and how to avoid the breaks. Just count up the days, contact your coach... then beat that number next time!

#buildthechain

MONDAY

January 15: An early morning Monday ramble.
Hit the ground running! Build the Chain!

What happens today is YOUR decision. No one else can influence how you think or react to situations. If you 'cocked up' this weekend, if you were lazy or if you chose not to take a step towards your goal... it's in the past. Move on and build a newer, stronger chain starting today!

If you kept your chain unbroken, awesome... you too need to move on and think about the actionable steps you can take today to keep it that way.

If we can create fear, frustration and doubt in our lives, then equally it's just as easy to create abundance, wealth and happiness. All it takes is a shift of mindset and a change of YOUR reaction to any situation. As I've said above, you can CHOOSE to react in a given way. You can choose to value yourself and continue on the path to a better body, a better happier version of yourself. Or you can choose to be grumpy, you can choose the path of anger and hate. I know which I prefer. I know which one I try to help people achieve.

I know which one most of the people reading this want to achieve!

Ramblings for Monday... out
#buildthechain

P.S. anyone with kids? Book recommendation for bedtime 'The Lion Inside'. Basic message: think like a winner and believe in yourself!

TUESDAY

January 16: A ramble as good as the chain!
The quest for happiness!

Happiness doesn't come from achievement. Think about it. It lasts for seconds. When I have a Ferrari, that will make me happy...

When I lift 100kg I'll be happy.
When I hit 60kg, I'll be happy.
When I run a 6-min mile, I'll be happy.
When I have a six-pack, I'll be happy...

It's so short-lived. It's still important to aim for and achieve the goals you set out because they will teach you, better you, make you healthier, give you abundance. What they won't actually bring you, however, is happiness. That comes from other things entirely, because otherwise every rich person (sliding scale) you see would have a big old smile on their face, and every poor person would be miserable. There are studies that show that people in third-world countries living off less than £20 per week are happier than those in first-world countries living off millions! Why?

The first reason is GRATITUDE.

I heard a great statement or way of thinking about this yesterday.

> Changing 'have-to's' into 'get-to's'
> People simply don't realise how lucky they are
> I have to go to the gym today...

I GET TO go to the gym today (and even have the opportunity to get healthier, live longer, get stronger).

> I have to take my child to gymnastics.
> I GET TO take my child to gymnastics.

How lucky is that, that I'm able to take my boy to something he enjoys and watch him (when I can, lol)?

I have to go to do the food shopping.

I GET TO go to a supermarket where they supply all the foods I need to stay healthy in one place, so that I can CHOOSE the foods I want (while there are people around the world who don't get a choice, and who have never eaten more than five different foods).

Perspective is a wonderful thing. When you start noticing and be grateful for the things you have, the mindset can switch.

The more grateful you are, the more your mindset will switch to one of happiness and positivity. A really simple way of viewing this is to do the following exercise:

- Give yourself 10 secs in the room you are in to count all the RED objects in the room. Count them all up. Then close your eyes.
- Then, with your eyes closed, try to remember how many blue items there were in the room... how many? Did you even notice the blue items?

Here's the point... we go about our lives complaining about what we don't have, what hardships we have, what we HAVE TO do today (the RED) objects. We, therefore, are not concentrating on and thus completely miss all the great things (the BLUE) objects we have in our lives.

So how can we change this?

Simple... every morning, state three things you are grateful for, and write them down.

The next morning, write down three more, but, hey, they can't be the same three. Keep this going day after day. How does it help? Well, once you've done a couple of days, you start looking for the 'blue objects'. They aren't always obvious like 'I'm grateful for my wife, my children and the roof over my head'... No, they could be, 'I'm grateful for the fact I get to listen to this song' or 'I'm grateful that I got to sit and have a coffee in a coffee shop in silence, watching the world go by'.

You seek out things to be grateful for, and the blue objects appear more and the red ones less. Suddenly there is a shift in mindset.

Ramblings out for today! Add to your chain each day the three things you are grateful for...
#buildthechain

WEDNESDAY

January 17: This morning I got to ramble in a very strong wind.

The difference between the person you are now and the person you want to be is that the person you want to BE is already doing all the things that you say you are going to DO!

We all have grand ideas of where we see ourselves in three months', six months' or a years' time, but the issue often arrives that you don't act like that person!

Let's say the person that I want to become owns their own house for example... so what does that person do that I don't do?

They are more organised with their finances, they know their margins, they know how much each month to the penny they can save, and they know how much they will need for x, y and z.

So, what would I need to do in order to know that information?

Monthly accounts were broken into categories.

Even better would be saying to myself: right, I need to make an allotted time slot per week where I sit down and do those figures.

THE PERSON YOU WANT TO BE ALREADY DOES THE THINGS YOU NEED TO DO!

Sp Adobe Spark

Now, once I put that slot into my diary, I then know I'm accountable for that time. If I don't do it, I've made a choice not to do it, and I can't complain when I get to the end of the month or year time frame and I haven't saved for each category on the spreadsheet.

As I own a gym, I often have people tell me their goals for their physique and strength.

Let's say someone wants to go from a size 16 to a size 10.

What does THAT size 10 version of you do that the size 16 person doesn't? That's the question to ask.

They go to the gym three times instead of two.

They eat 85% whole foods vs 15%... naughty but nice.

They are not a slave to the scales... they know their goal is a size 10, not 66kg (random figure btw).

So now you can see what this new version of you does that you do differently, you now have the CHOICE to do it... or not. If you choose not to do it, well in six months' time you look back and you know the reason.

Here's the thing – you have to record this stuff. Write down the goal, write down how you're going to get there, hold yourself accountable. Don't be afraid to fail that, of course… make the decision NOT TO. Build the Chain towards that new version of yourself. Remember you GET TO try to do these things, you don't have to… don't waste your time with negativity and want… go out and get it. Put things in place that will see you succeed, rather than talking about them and half acting on it. Be grateful for what you have and what you can have!

#buildthechain
Rambling out, it's officially f'ing freezing, eye-streaming wind #pleasant

THURSDAY

January 18

This morning's ramblings take a break from the mindset and move on to a question asked on our private forum for our members. But it does tie in with the question:

How do I set myself a goal that's relative to my current level of fitness?

Lots of people are at very different stages of their fitness and health journey. Most people have an 'end point' in mind (in inverted commas, because the needle shifts constantly, especially when you get there and don't even realise that you've got there!)

It's ok to have grand goals, big ones, ones that seem impossible. If they are impossible, it's the job of your coach to tell you… more from a sporting standpoint. A 35-year-old rugby player playing for Bognor Regis is not going to suddenly push out George Ford from his starting place in the England rugby team.

Adobe Spark

You set realistic targets.

Then you put the necessary actionable steps in place in order to get there.

Want to shave two hours off your Ironman time? It's possible. With the right plan of training, the right changes to nutrition, the right accessory strength programme and the right physical therapy support, you CAN get there. You break the goal down into steps... actionable processes:

- Run X number of times per week
- Swim Y number of times
- Bike Z number of miles

Then go further and give them times, speeds, distances per minutes, etc.

The more detailed the process and the more you stick to it, the more the accumulative workload transforms your body, your machine, into the person able to shave two hours off their time.

Goal setting is about looking at where you want to be, putting the necessary steps in place in order to get there, and then actually following through! 'Pay the man', as they say.

So how do you set goals for your current fitness level? You look at where you want to end up. Then get help in designing the right plan to get there. Along the way, have phases of 'testing' and keep a record of everything, so that you can see the improvements. If each month you sit down and flick back through your diary and you see everything going up, and your times are improving, you know you're on track. If you don't keep a record and you can't see the improvements, then the chances are your goal will always stay on the horizon!

Who would be interested in a goal setting download sheet? One to help you plan out your goal in greater detail?

Ramblings for today over and out... jumping over fallen bins, as the wind is gale force!

FRIDAY

January 19: Today's ramblings are more reflection... this week... coming a little later due to a child seat muck-up.

It's been a great week. The response to the post about perspective has been amazing. I've had countless people tell me they read it and that they were suddenly 'noticing all the blue'. Not just people in the gym but people who I didn't even know read the ramblings.

THE
PICTURE
THAT
DESCRIBES
MY
WEEK

Sp Adobe Spark

I wrote to all gym members past and present, and loads asked for it to be sent to them via their email. I always say these things are worth writing even if just one person uses it to better themselves. The fact that more than one person utilises it is amazing.

This week has been a really focused week. Why? Because I myself utilised the act of goal setting. I decided on an outcome goal, and then developed the process goals by which to get there. Suddenly the outcome goal is moving closer and closer.

For those who have missed what those terms mean:

An 'outcome goal' is a big goal, the measurable end goal. Things like lose 30lbs, get a six-pack and win a competition.

The next step of the process really is to ask yourself why you want that goal. Ask it three times and answer differently each time. This will give you the ammunition when the going gets tough.

Then comes the 'process goals'. The how to go about achieving the goals.

Take the 14kg weight loss as an example of what things you need to do in order to achieve the outcome goal:

Go to the gym Monday/Wednesday/Friday
Eat three meals a day, made up of XYZ
Drink X number of glasses of water
Three measurable (tickable) processes through which
you can stay accountable.

Do them daily/weekly and you will put yourself in the BEST POSSIBLE place to achieve your outcome. Not only that, they are steps towards the person you want to be!

So, what happens now? Well, we have Friday today, so the processes continue, and then Saturday will be a refine the processes day. I'll have a look at what worked and what didn't, and then adjust for the week after. I'm after constant improvement, not gratification. There is always more, the job is never done... that's the enjoyment of it, a never-ending quest for improvement. What will I do when the outcome goal is reached? I'll create another, a bigger one, one that brings more excitement and learning opportunities!

What were your most successful processes this week?

What picture shows how this week has gone for you? Mine is a picture of Lillie in her child seat... maybe post the picture in your timeline with the hashtag #buildthechain. After all, the chain we are building is meant to be worldwide, and what better place to start than a picture that paints your words!

Ramblings out for this week – happy Friday people!

SATURDAY

January 21

Ｎo rambles on a Saturday, but how about a pic that describes your week... post it on social media with.

#buildthechain

MONDAY

January 22: This morning's ramble is about
PRESSURE!

We all encounter it... at work, at home, our time, in the sport. But assuming it's not because of a lack of discipline, I've got a new way to think about PRESSURE!

Pressure is a privilege.

Think about it. Whenever you have pressure on you, look at the situation. Why do you have pressure on you?

BECAUSE IT MATTERS!

It means that you or someone else you know or care for believes in you.

You have a job... there's pressure on you. Why? Because you are the person they are relying on to take the company forwards in your area. They believe in you, and the pressure is there because they know you can handle the workload.

A surgeon performing surgery has pressure on him or her... to perform the act that they have trained to do, that they have chosen to do. The thing they should LOVE to do.

There is pressure in sport, the weight of a nation on the shoulders. You have reached the pinnacle of your career, you've done all the work, you have earned your place through dedication. Not many people will ever get the chance to stand in front of 85,000 fans of the sport you play. The pressure is a privilege.

Pressure exists in family life... let's be honest you are blessed to have a family, end of that one!

In any situation you have already won, you won the genetic lottery and got a chance at this life. Pressure most of the time is our perception of a given situation. We often build the pressure in our own minds because we all know that when the pressure is on, we act. There is a technique you can actually use to create pressure in order to get things done more effectively and more efficiently. It's called the 'Pomodoro Effect'.

Simply, it's creating a time 'pressure' on a given task in order to focus the mind and to give the task an 'end' point. Think back to the pressure of a deadline at school. If you are anything like me, you never did the essay when you got given it... no, you waited, waited until the deadline was the next day or even that afternoon. You wait to build pressure, then you perform. It's actually a natural human thing to do.

The next time you have pressure on you and something to do, remember firstly, it's a privilege that YOU GET TO DO THAT THING. And secondly, if you need pressure in order to get something, usually mundane, done... use the Pomodoro to add pressure. Set the timer and off you go...

We use it all the time in our workouts. Why do you think we use time-caps and timers? More work in less time... the pressure it creates makes us perform!

Ramblings out actual rambling today, as I was a wee bit late, but the pressure of knowing people are reading this got me to get it done... it's a privilege, you see, that people read and take note. A privilege to impact lives!

Have a great Monday and continue to build a better life...
#buildthechain

TUESDAY

January 23

Ramblings this Tuesday morning as we wake up to another working day!! Here's a useful phrase to remember: 'Improvements are intoxicating'.

There's nothing more enjoyable and more intoxicating than success and seeing improvements. It's why I emphasise keeping a journal for loads of different aspects of life.

Training is an easy one. You look back at what you did last week, your last workout, the last time you did the same workout and you see improvement. That moment you realise you are improving is the most, to me, intoxicating and self-motivating thing there is. Why? Because no one else got me there. It was all down to me... my body, my work, my method, my grit and determination. No one else can give you or hand you that improvement. People can help you along the way, or perhaps a programme that you clicked with. The right volume and intensity combined to bring out the best improvement, but you still have to get under the bar. Money can't buy you that happiness, only work pays that man!

Nutrition journals, looking back and seeing that you have stuck to the plan, can be intoxicating. Though a lot of people I've helped might prefer the other intoxicating stuff... they might not want to journal down on a Saturday night! It is, however, hugely

empowering to know that you fed yourself according to the plan. You made yourself feel better, with more energy and more strength from the food and water you consumed.

It's intoxicating to consistently tick off progress – it becomes amazing. That's when your transformation appears, where it 'clicks into place'... so let the improvements be your focus, not the outcome at the very end. Look for the small things along the way, as they will end up being the things you are most proud of!

Ramblings out for a Tuesday! Till tomorrow...
#buildthechain

WEDNESDAY

January 24

Sp Adobe Spark

This morning's ramblings are about a subject that is simple but misunderstood. It's about FEAR! Fear isn't always a bad thing though.

To make it simple, there are two types of fear: one is a good fear, the other is the one that is limiting.

The first fear is a rational fear. Think of it as protection fear. It's a reaction designed to protect you. It heightens your alertness, it increases your heart rate and dumps adrenaline into your body.

To a certain extent, you can then train yourself to fight or flight! You wake up in the middle of the night and hear a sound downstairs... that feeling where suddenly you are awake, heart pumping, called to action. Think spiders and bananas – RATIONAL FEARS.

The other fear is the irrational fear. This is the one that keeps you from living! The issue with this lies in the fact that, while both types of fear cause that same reaction in your body – the sweating, the heart pumping, the adrenaline – the irrational one has a thought attached to it!

Did you know what the biggest fear on the planet is? Public speaking! More people are scared of public speaking than dying!!! Completely irrational, huh! I am a self-confessed public speaking irrational fear holder. Weird, considering that at school I was ADHD and always seeking attention in any room... I've never had a bad experience speaking, but we build up these fears and insecurities along the way.

In the fitness industry, we see this irrational fear OFTEN! There will be multiple people reading this who will have experienced the irrational fear of walking through the door into a gym, the one that they use to delay going for weeks, months, years. Lots of people fear that they will be judged... what if I make a mistake or what if I do something incorrectly? Here's the thing... no one actually judges you. You fear they do, but in actual fact they aren't watching you, they aren't hoping you slip up. They are remembering that they too were a beginner once. It's irrational, because 99.99999% of the time no one has ever said anything to you in the gym. It's an insecurity that has built up and that has manifested itself in the unwillingness to take the next step. Delaying until you're fitter, delaying until the 'right' time, ...

So, what do you do? Firstly, you need to recognise the fear – it's yours. What do you do with it? You process it and accept it as an irrational fear, like the one I have of ANY spider. If you have ever thought that you want to go to a gym and get fit, that is your indication to reach out! Out there is a gym that will embrace you, guide you, help you realise that the gym is a place to conquer your fears and give you strength in ALL aspects of life. A strong body and a strong mind! Trust that you can get past the fear. We have a chat with most of our members before they join, to try and help them settle in straight away. We suggest certain sessions and certain times of day, and we offer a fundamental session to understand how the gym operates, from the timetable to the different classes. We take the time to do this because we know everyone has a goal that they are trying to achieve but have things holding them back... usually, an irrational fear or self-imposed limitation. Want to overcome it? The first step is to recognise and own that fear. As soon as you do, reach out and let's break it down!

Was in two minds whether to post this... I feared it wasn't good enough. But, hey, I'm overcoming the irrational fear of being judged. If you're reading this, it's because you want to... fear conquered!

Ramblings out for another day!
#buildthechain

THURSDAY

January 25

I've been thinking about this rambling since Monday, when I ran the idea past someone... they looked at me as if I'd come from Mars, but they always do, so I thought I'd write it anyway!

An exercise for when you are feeling SHIT!!
It's called the BE POSITIVE COFFEE.
It's simple really, though you will need a few things to do it.
You'll need:

- £5
- A pen
- A diary or sheet of paper
- An hour
- Your Stevia

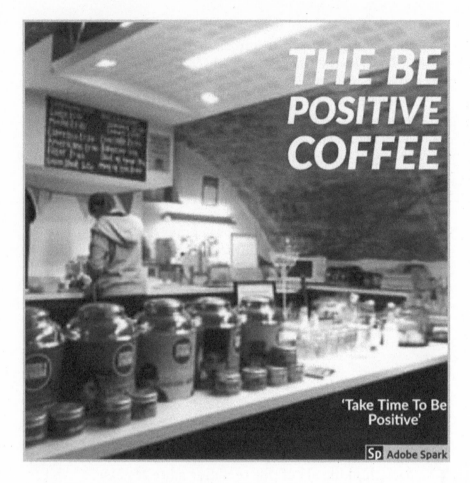

Here's what you have to do:

Find a coffee shop that has a window overlooking a street or at street level so you can see people walking by. Preferably a busy street with at least a flow of 10 people per minute past the window. Also, you want to find one with a comfy chair... you're there for up to an hour, so you don't want a numb bum!

(Parents I know you struggle like I do to find an hour, but try to find it. Ask your other half for that time... if you need it, you need it.)

Order a coffee/tea/relaxing beverage.

Sit in the window seat, alone, and put on a set of headphones (you don't have to have anything playing... it acts as a barrier, to stop people bothering you, this is YOUR time).

Get out your diary/paper.

For each person you NOTICE (that's important because you have to let your brain tell you where to look), write down a positive thought about that person.

Start simple:

- I like their shoes, hair, jacket. Superficial things are an easy start.

Then expand if you can, going into things like:

- They look happy.
- They look like they have a spring in their step.

Look for positives that otherwise you may brush over.

Old people holding hands is a nice one... the fact that after years of ups and downs, they still seek each other's touch as a security and show of love.

Small minute details of positivity.

So, what does this weird exercise do? Well, have you ever tried not letting a negative thought enter your body for an hour? Can you honestly say that after an hour of focusing on positivity, you wouldn't come out of that coffee shop with a new positive mindset?

Imagine, if you will, if the next 10 people you met had all done the same. Imagine if they had only looked for positive things before meeting up with you... the world would be a VERY different place to live!

This follows on a fair bit from one of the previous ramblings about looking for and being grateful for the positive things we are fortunate enough to have.

So, if you are feeling crap it's probably because you have let outside influences affect your mind. You can choose to change this by hitting RESET. All you need is a cuppa and a pen and piece of paper.

#buildthechain

Friday

January 26

Friday ramblings are really about the reflection of the week past, so I'll share a real-life story!

So, Tuesday morning is a great example of me changing my mindset and ability to cope with situations. Ones that in the past would have affected my entire day and probably longer.

I'll set the scene.

It's 4.50am... my alarm goes off. Quickly change and let Chase (our dog) out. Grab my food for the day and my coffee, lock Chase back in his cage and head out the door for the 9-min drive to work.

Couple miles down the road there is a corner where usually people will cut the corner and essentially be in the middle of the road. Everyone does it... I do it. Just so happens someone was doing it and hadn't seen my headlights – they had theirs on full beam and stayed in the middle of the road. No choice for me but to shift over to the left. In doing so, my brand-new alloy scrapes the kerb, not a little, like all the way around the rim. That type where you pucker up a little and go... fuuuuuuu****k!

Got out and checked it wasn't cracked. Nope, just scraped the whole way around. Ouch!

Previously in my life it would have REALLY pissed me off. I'd probably have been in a foul mood and it genuinely would have annoyed me all day.

But over my learning and from hanging around with people who have had a positive impact on my mindset, I used the following coping mechanism:

- Thought
- Appreciate
- Process
- Embrace
- Let it go

I thought about it, I appreciated it had happened, I processed the thought, I embraced or recognised the FEELING of annoyance, but then... I let it go.

Here's the thing, I can't now affect what has happened... it's happened. What I can do is be in control of how I REACT to it. It's a choice to be angry... or I can recognise that I can't affect the fact it's happened and in fact appreciate that I can have it fixed, that I'm still alive and that money can fix it. It's a possession, that's it. I'm lucky I even have a car! It's my choice to have one, my choice to put my money towards one, and my choice to pay for the running costs!

It seems simple but we do it so often. We don't recognise the feelings we have – instead, we let them own us, we let them affect the rest of our thoughts, because we don't make time to recognise that they are there and that we can affect them.

Fear – see yesterday… the post is a huge one. How many times have you not done something out of fear and how many times have you been held back? I've done it loads. But at the time of that fear, have I been able to apply the above principles? Nope, I've let the fear steer my decision.

Guilt, it's stunning many a fat-loss client. They eat something they perceive to be naughty, they feel guilty about it, and they give up.

Instead, they could eat it, recognise why they wanted it, recognise the guilt as an indication that they want more for themselves, talk about it or process that feeling, embrace that, and let it go. Move on and not let it affect the rest of the plan.

As this is the last one of the week, perhaps look back at the week. Have you acted out of fear? Have you let something affect you all day that you could have perhaps reacted to differently? If so, prepare yourself for next time, and start looking at your thoughts and feelings with the above in mind. Fairly sure that your days may become more positive!

#buildthechain

MONDAY

January 29

Ah, the Monday morning rambles. Been expanding my sources of enlightenment in the last year or so.

Occasionally, I listen to experts in industries other than the fitness industry. I think we can learn from a multitude of industries, take qualities from them and then apply them in our own way.

"YOU REAP WHAT YOU SOW"

SD Adobe Spark

There will always be something that is relevant to the fitness or health industry.

Farming (was researching quality of foods)... the cows always need feeding, you have to show up every day! Planning and preparation bring the harvest... you can't simply wing it. Looking ahead, planning sometimes up to years in advance, is necessary to have a great harvest. Playing the long game and occasionally leaving things fallow will bring a bumper harvest next year!

Sometimes you have to leave one element with minimal volume in order to bring up some of the other elements. Strength can take years to build. Olympic lifting is a prime example. It takes YEARS of dedicated practice to master those lifts. (We're talking Games and regional athletes here.) Leaving some of the cardio behind in order to gain expert status in the lifts is a little bit like crop rotation in the fields – planting something now so that the end product is that much more valuable. Obviously, if you're not after Games status, then you can keep a fairly level amount of work in each area and bring them all up slowly but surely. I would still, however, recommend spending more time on your weaknesses than your strengths!

Farming, I think, is very similar to fitness in some respects... show up, do the work, plan and set goals and then Build the Chain. Break the chain (don't feed the cows or water the crops) and the process takes longer. If disease or weeds grow externally or internally, find something to either offer protection beforehand or stamp the weeds yourself. You have to get your hands dirty and no one is going to do it for you.

Want to know where your weaknesses lie and therefore the biggest opportunity for improvement? It's usually the one aspect you fear the most... it could be the one that you dislike the most. Usually, people dislike something because they are not good at it... the vicious cycle! Plan... dedicate six weeks to it, track the improvement, follow the ACTUAL progressions, have a coach look at the weaknesses and help you navigate and record the improvement. Much like the fields, you reap what you sow!

Rambles over for the day. Tasks for today... identify a weakness, plan a way to improve it, execute the plan and Build the Chain!

#buildthechain

TUESDAY

January 30: Uh oh! WRITERS BLOCK!

For the morning rambles, it's often a phrase or conversation that I have listened to that gives me the inspiration for the subject

WHEN YOU HAVE NO INSPIRATION... JUST TURN UP!

Sp Adobe Spark

I write about. It's almost like revision. However, sometimes I don't have that powerful message that I hear and want to spread.

What happens then? Do I not bother, or do I continue with my meditation of walking and writing? You never know if just by getting out there in the crisp am air something might come to me and I may think of something.

It's probably similar to when things go wrong with people's goals, like in nutrition when you don't have all the ingredients, or you haven't done your meal prep and you get stuck at work. You could just say to yourself 'oh well, it's screwed up, I'll just go get some pie and chips', or you could FOLLOW YOUR PRINCIPLES of the person you want to become and go to the shops, get something healthier, something in line with your goals, and carry on the quest!

In training it's like turning up to the gym and all the racks being used. Some people would turn around and go, 'oh well I can't train, I'll just go home'. But the person who is clear about their goal and about who they want to be will perhaps move on to the next exercise. They will note in their training diary that they had to do Y before X this time, and still put everything into it.

We all have those moments, those unclear moments... no inspiration, no driving factor other than our own 'I said I would do this'.

I said at the beginning of the year that if I was fit and able, I would go out every morning and get something written, a ramble. Today I had nothing to write about, so that's what I wrote about. It's ok to have those days of doubt – you can still make them useful days, you can still Build the Chain, and you can still further yourself as a person. You just have to recognise the opportunity.

For those interested, I've been listening to a lot of info on glute transformation... any females (although I'm sure there are a few guys that might also benefit, both for strength and aesthetics) ready to transform that body part should apply below... you'll need to be able to train at least two times a week and for six weeks uninterrupted.

In the meantime, happy Tuesday rambles for the day over... not bad considering I had nothing to write about!

#buildthechain

WEDNESDAY

January 31

Next in the rambling series of what I've learnt from other industries is a well-known one.

The building industry!

The most obvious, but often the most forgotten or taken for granted, rule is that the most important part of building a house is

to build your foundations deep enough and strong enough to withstand the environment around it and the pressure from above!

Go back a stage from that, though, and I'd say it's also damn important to choose your location for those foundations wisely, do your research and get recommendations as to the quality of the ground you're going to build on! We are lucky in this technology-driven era that reviews are left about businesses for us to see and search. Do the groundwork! It's why we're so proud of the fact we've only got 5* reviews for our business so far. That means the gym we've built has the solid ground and firm rock for YOU to lay your foundations on! First thing today is to always do your research, but don't let it be a delay tactic!

So, the foundations on which we can build our health and fitness: There's the obvious...

- Nutrition
- Training frequency
- Activity daily
- Lifestyle choices

But there are some more subtle foundations too...

Enjoyment, you need to feel a sense of enjoyment from it, whether that's the fun while you're doing it or the 'it's fun once I've finished' feeling.

Is it sustainable? If you're building your foundations and you start to question whether it's sustainable, perhaps you are starting to build before you've finished the foundations? Remember, the foundations are the start points, the minimum, the thing to build upon. So, if you start and you think it's too much, back off a bit... you can always return to more later!

So, what would good foundations look like?

Nutrition – here are some key factors:

- Getting enough protein in order to recover from your training.
- Match your calories to your goal.
- Eat enough fats to drive your hormonal system.
- Eat carbohydrates according to your activity level.
- Ensure half your plate is vegetables.

There is one theme that ALL good nutrition plans promote: eat plenty of vegetables... the wider the variety, the better!

Training frequency is important. You have to be realistic and commit to the number of sessions you can do. Worse than not training effectively is not turning up... don't commit to four days if you can only do two. It comes down to the sustainable part. Some can lay their foundations on five days a week, while some have to settle for two. However many sessions you build on, make those sessions efficient and get the most out of them. Two great sessions are better than four mediocre ones!

For those who can't train more days, you can aim for greater DAILY ACTIVITY. That means taking more steps, not sitting down as much, walking places, playing. The more active you are, the fitter and more energetic you will be!

Lifestyle choices I don't have time to go into today, but we're looking at removing things like smoking and unnecessarily consuming alcohol.

A lot of people skip the foundations and think immediately about the house and the fancy furnishings. Remember, though, the stronger the foundations, the more likely it is that that house is going to stay up for years to come. Skip the foundations... be prepared to pick up some bricks later on!

Foundation ramblings out...
#buildthechain

THURSDAY

February 1: Ramblings for today
'Why I love CrossFit'.

A CrossFit gym is not a gym where you just go to work out. It's a place you make friends, get to know people and completely change your mindset about what it is to be healthy and what it means to exercise. It takes away the mundane, it takes away the loneliness, it takes away bravado. It prioritises progression, it encourages community, it brings fun to fitness, it brings variety and thus rids boredom. It has no room for egos, it humbles you and elates you all in one day. You can match it to your goals while also becoming stronger mentally and emotionally.

What is CrossFit in layman's terms?

Basically, it's a type of fitness that makes you look fantastic, improves your health and increases your confidence, while surrounded by a group of people all looking for the same thing you are. All this is led by a coach who's there with one purpose... to ensure that you get through every session having improved. It's

the building and improving that leads to the results... you turn up, you improve daily, and hey presto the results come.

Short one today... hands got cold!

#buildthechain

Want to try a CrossFit class wherever you are? Just message me. I can even try and get in touch with your local box, and see if you can have a try for free... worth asking, hey!

FRIDAY

February 2: Friday rambles!
It's not about the muscle!

The PROCESS of building the physique you want and the body to perform is the true benefit!

The character you develop, the sacrifices, the weaknesses you overcome... you overcome your own laziness. The ability to see an obstacle you previously would have been fearful of, and you attack it. That confidence and control of your life! (Ultimately, it's not the actual physique that brings you pleasure, but the processes by which you get there teach you and your own body what GREAT feels like!)

Being extremely lean (believe me I've been there) doesn't bring happiness, but appreciating the processes and what it taught you in getting there has immeasurable benefits.

On the outside, the goal of developing a great physique has its benefits, but this is only true if you allow it to. It gives you the confidence to attack your fears and overcome your weaknesses, BUT only if you appreciate the processes by which you get there. For example, you develop control of your nutrition, you develop a schedule by which you can maintain and enjoy, you do things that scare you. If your biggest weakness is the food you put in your mouth, then in order to achieve the goal, you're going to have to address the weakness. If your biggest fear is stepping into a gym for the first time, then to get the physique you desire you're going to have to address the fear. If you have a partner who is trying to hold you back through their own insecurities, then you will have to address the problem.

So, building muscle or getting lean isn't all about the end result. It's about making a version of you that is more confident in the ability to tackle ANYTHING. It's about standing up to your demons, and it's about nourishing yourself not only with food but also with happiness. It's about developing the proactive habits, it's about waking up in the morning with a purpose and a guide, but with the freedom to make your own path.

Developing great principles and then habits from the principles leads to greatness, both mentally and physically. The article is never finished... as you get older, the processes have to change with the times, your physique will change as a reflection of the care you give to it. Challenges will come, but if your habits and principles by which you live are solid, you will always be confident in the fact you are doing your best, you are in control of what life throws at you, and by and large you are prepared for anything.

Happy Friday people, have a great weekend, build on the good habits, Build the Chain, attack a weakness and laugh a lot!

#buildthechain

SATURDAY

February 3: Saturday means no rambles, just a little something that describes the week!

A monthly PB board at the gym all filled up means one thing... every single one of those people took a giant leap towards their goals. But it doesn't tell you the story of many other people who all took massive steps too, whether physical or mental. So, although a PB board has a story behind it, there's a mass of people who did equally well and who deserve to get their name up there soon!

Is it potentially worth creating your very own PB board? You could see the month filling up with all of the things you achieved. Surrounding yourself with positivity is a path to a more positive mind!

#buildthechain

MONDAY

February 5

Rambles for a Monday. I think this weekend saw the most phrases or thoughts that could turn into potential rambles...

At the top level, sport naturally selects the best... basically, to be the very best at something, the naturally strongest, most suited people will thrive. Now, I'm going to use CrossFit as the conversation here as the competitive side grows. Let's take Mat Fraser and Katrin... I was listening to a podcast with Ben Bergeron, their coach.

The topic moved to the sheer volume and work capacity they have – it's off the scale, it's like nothing you could imagine. Now, they both had blood work done periodically and guess what? Even at those training intensities and volumes, their bloodwork was exceptional, and their cortisol to testosterone levels bang in balance and still at the good end of the spectrum. The difference between us and them? Well, ours would tank, cortisol would break us down, and we wouldn't even be able to withstand the training. It allows them to cope with a workload that we mortals cannot handle... it allows them to keep getting better, while we would crumble. I think it's true of any sport, though. Those who can withstand the demands and not crumble will succeed.

So, what does it mean for us mere mortals? What it means is that we have to match our training volumes and intensities not to that of the best, but to that which we can withstand. Ideally, we would use bloodwork among other biomarkers to work out whether it should be least mode or beast mode (the last mode is a term taken from the writings and teachings of Luke Leaman of Muscle Nerds, a fantastic educational company offering great interviews on a podcast). What should we watch for if we don't have access to or don't want to use these things? Grip strength, perceived alertness and readiness to train would be things that, if you are in tune with yourself, you could monitor.

Another mentor of mine, AJ Roberts, has a great explanation of things to look for... the body's callings, the small voice that gives us a clue that something isn't right. What may start as a small niggle is the first sign, and whether we choose to hear it or ignore it is our choice. Maybe after that, some tendon issues arise, a slightly louder voice that we still choose to ignore perhaps. Then comes a full-blown rupture, a screaming you can't ignore. We have to listen and recognise the 'inner voices', understand our capabilities and improve on them. Nowadays, with social media and the human tendency, we shoot straight for the best, we naturally navigate towards the 'freak' in order to emulate or put down those people, as our own capabilities don't allow us to get there. For those who are inspired, be inspired, but know your capabilities may not match those of a genetic outlier... use their principles as a guide but do not copy! For those who are negatively affected or then spread hate towards the best, know you are you... you don't need to put them down to make yourself feel better. Simply look at your own capabilities and push them forwards in your own way. You are just as valuable, perhaps at showing the less fortunate genetically that they can still improve dramatically against all odds!

As the sport of CrossFit grows towards its 10th year as a recognised sport, we are starting to see trends in the sport (more on this to come). What will always be true is that the very best will come from a genetic predisposition we will be unaware of until the work is also applied. That's why it's a great sport... you can't rely on genetics and you still have to work hard, but when genetics meet work ethic, something amazing is produced!

Rambles out. This week, unless I hear something that sparks a different direction, there will be quite a few rambles in CrossFit in general. It's still growing, maybe in different directions to that originally intended, but I can't see any other fitness movement in the last eight years that has had such an impact on people's lives. It's here to stay... in what capacity? Well, that will be led by the consumer!

TUESDAY

February 6: Ah, the Tuesday rambles could be another fine one!

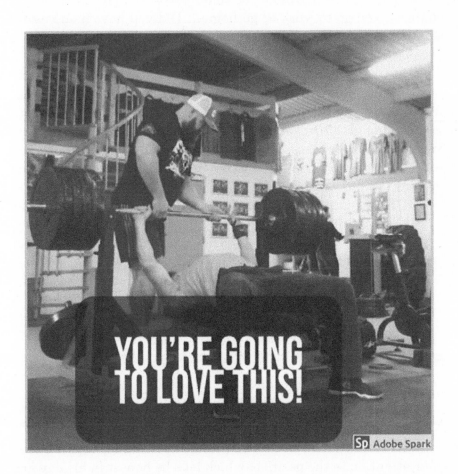

YOU'RE GOING TO LOVE THIS!

Sp Adobe Spark

The art of pausing a reflection and REflection task. (That's right I just made up a word... what you going to do about it?)

In today's world, everything is rushed – travel, eating, reading, internet loading times, training. This is probably due to the finite time we have and that constant pressure to get things done!

However, I believe there are two instances where we miss an opportunity to stop and centre ourselves. Two times when, if we took 2–3 mins, we would further ourselves as students of fitness and we would ultimately save time down the line AND raise our self-awareness. I want to bring into YOUR training something that I have learnt from using the 5-min journal but adapted to training.

Imagine getting to the gym before or after work. You're rushed, you have a window of time, you start, you lift, you get changed, you go to work or go home... Did you have a successful session? You don't really know.

Here's another way you could go about training...

...at work, at the gym, in the car using 'Siri'. Predetermine what would make a GREAT, training session. Three things that would mean you would walk away from that session satisfied that you had got closer to your goals and done it in an enjoyable way. What does this do? It centres your mind on the task and allows you to focus in on what you need to do, but it also allows you to start making the process enjoyable.

Do the session that you're prescribed by your coach or programme.

REflection time.

End of the session, starts to APPRECIATE your accomplishments.

Write out the three things you accomplished in your session.

> Weight lifted
> Rest period adhered to
> Execution of a lift
> The flow of a lift
> Done with a smile
> Literally anything.

This REflection serves a two-pronged benefit. Firstly, it brings your attention to the positive, which let's be honest in his day and age we need! And secondly, it serves to bring a mental end to training. Like making the bed in the morning is to a sleep routine and unmaking it at night, this REflection brings an end to training. You can't affect it now, but what you can do is appreciate the positives and highlight them.

So, there it is... the next stage of the #buildthechain series of tasks. You have the power of adherence through building consistency, and now you have the power of PRE and RE flection... which I should have spelt 'flexion' (get it?) just to annoy my grammar trolls. So here it is:

The preflexion and reflexion for your training gains. Notice what is good, focus the mind and reap the results!!

Personally, I think this ramble is genius. It's taken a really successful method of journaling and applied it straight to YOUR needs. Be happy!

#buildthechain

WEDNESDAY

February 7

For an answer you may seek, it is precisely where you are not looking.

Wednesday rambles,
Minus 1 million
Reflecting on childhood
I remember as a kid a saying that used to be thrown around.

'The sign of madness is repeatedly doing the same thing, but expecting a different outcome.'

If only we would remember that this applies to fitness and health too!

How many times have you gone into a massive calorie restriction and lost a load of weight, but then bounced right back to where you were before or even higher?

How many times have you put in the effort to go five days a week to the gym and hated every minute of it, or gone on holiday, come back and waited till two months before your next visit to the gym? Not only are you wasting the money in between, but aren't you also feeling like you're starting again?

It may present itself differently each time, but ultimately you are rinsing and repeating, expecting that this time it will be different... you will keep the result.

Well, here's the thing. Over the years it's become apparent that those who truly are not mad, those who learn the processes and principles, and those who develop the process-orientated approach are the ones who succeed long term. Those who address their weaknesses and don't see them as failures, who see them instead as opportunities for self-development, are the ones who a) achieve anything they want and b) remain where they want.

Those who fixated on the outcome for feelings of worth, trying to create an armour against their insecurity, are the ones who don't realise the madness. In fact, often they will go mad and become depressed and anxious.

Although it seems harder, those who work on the internal environment are the ones who change their entire lives in the long term. Those who work exclusively on the external without challenging their internal will always feel resentment and never truly be happy.

Fitness can be your greatest learning tool for both internal and external. It can drive confidence, strength and perseverance, but it has just as much value in teaching you to work, think, adapt, integrate and laugh. Enjoy the process... find something you can be excited about WITH people who build you up but challenge your thinking.

Above all else learn to LOVE them
PROCESSES AND the outcome.
Ramblings out!

#buildthechain

THURSDAY

February 8: Think you're unlucky? Guess again!

Thursday rambles is a gratefulness one. As a gym owner and PT, I've seen people depressed, elated, nervous, happy, scared, confident, ... it's normal on a daily basis to see ALL of these 'states'.

UNLUCKY... ARE YOU FREAKING
KIDDING ME!

Sp Adobe Spark

The one that I think most don't realise is how lucky they actually are. I was listening to the former bodybuilder turned entrepreneur Ben Pakulski talk the other day on his change of mindset and thinking since a) leaving the professional bodybuilding scene and b) having his kids. The latter, I think, has a huge effect on anyone mentally... the moment they are born, this wave of love like no other, this completely helpless need to do better as a person for them and to teach them. Anyway... I digress.

We often consider that we are lucky to be here. Out of millions of sperm swimming around, it was ours that fought the battle and had the perseverance to get to that one chosen egg that dropped at that one particular time... that one egg that has been within your mother from the moment she was born. How utterly incredible is that! But then take it one stage further. In order for that to happen, both your parents had to be born, at the precise moments they were. One day delay and they would not have been there... YOU would not have been here. Yes, that means your grand-parents' parents also had to have had sex at that one particular moment, that day, that hour, that minute (or less – ewwwwww...). It blows my mind the precise amount of LUCK that had to occur for ME to be here. Not only that, but the luck as well that my wife and I were born at our particular moments, which has allowed us to create two amazing children who we will get to teach, guide, love and observe. They will show us our shortcomings as they grow up, they will take our good and bad habits, and they will display in themselves, like a mirror, our ethics and values. Even more amazing is that from them the next generation may come. Lillie already has within her about 1 million eggs, which contain half the genetic code for my granddaughter or grandson... MIND F'ING BLOWN!

So, when you're having that day where you are feeling unlucky, read the above again and realise the chance of you being here was smaller than anything you could imagine.

Deep this is, but feeling lucky. All that luck for 80–100 years of life (hopefully)... I don't plan on squandering it!

#buildthechain

FRIDAY

February 9: Friday rambles!

Two forgotten elements of goal setting... after listening to a great podcast on goal setting.

Adobe Spark

We've set our goals, we've worked out the plan, we've set up the processes. We feel good, we're on track, we are building our chain.

Then comes two hours of sleep a night because your child has flu or you have to stay up late to collect your loved one from the airport. Perhaps you get stuck at work and then it's raining and dark, but you are meant to be doing your training runs for that Ironman that you have set as your goal. These are the occasions that you need to a) plan for, and b) use the following phrases and write them down:

- I am the person who goes out for that training run when I get home late and it's pissing with rain.

- I am the person who gets up early and still goes to the gym when my child has been up all night.
- I am the person who makes time to collect my loved one, but also then gets my training done.

You attach IDENTITY to the action. No one wants to let themselves down... you want to be that person, so start telling yourself you *are* that person. You are, after all, the sum of your habits. If you say you are, you are. If you build that character trait, you will become!

The second element of goal setting quite often not talked about is that fact that purely setting a goal is EXCITING – it makes you feel great. Why? Because you're envisaging a new you! One that is who you want to be, rather than accepting you as you are. What's more exciting than a better and more confident version of yourself? The part that people forget is the EXECUTION of that goal. It's all great talking about it... now you have to keep that promise to yourself and, as Nike say, 'Just Do It'.

#buildthechain

SATURDAY

February 10

Saturday... no rambles, just REflection and gratitude. Good luck to our community and followers, have a great weekend, build your chain and keep your goals in mind!

What went well is a great place to start your REflection...

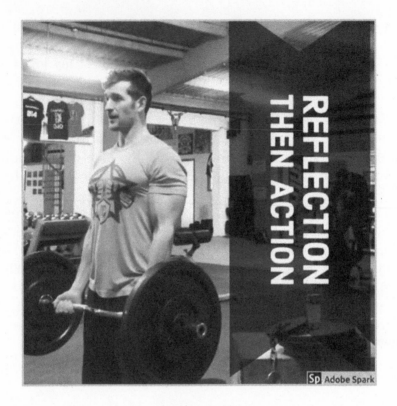

#buildthechain

MONDAY

*February 12: Monday rambles
at minus 2!*

Is the fitness industry moving away from health and moving towards extremism?

Health is actually quite hard to define and also quite hard to actually SEE. On a biological level, you'd be looking at cellular

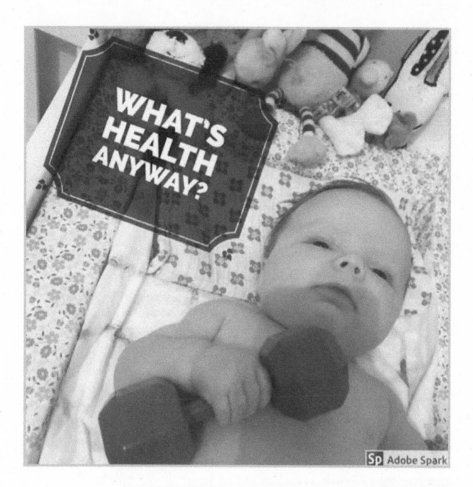

Sp Adobe Spark

health – basically, if your cells are in an optimum state, you're healthy. But that's quite hard for us general pop to see currently! Instead, we have these outward markers.

As with anything, we usually look to the top for indication of our current status. Could this be the wrong thing to do?

Take sports. Most people assume these professionals are healthy. Well, turns out if you look at the top of the field, quite often this isn't true.

Powerlifting... quite often the top guys have too many health problems to count.

CrossFit... perhaps too early to tell, but at some point the countless hours of training and competition are going to pass the health point into the overuse and potential injury realms.

Bodybuilding... you are judged at your most unhealthy point.

Rugby... the pros these days pretty much sign up for a car crash each game, and probably average at least a couple injuries a season.

So, basically, we can't look at the top of the sport for health. So where to look? Is there a point at which we don't need to do 'more' – lift more, run more, get stronger, get leaner, etc?

I believe there is, but I don't know what that is yet. Perhaps it changes over time, and you can be healthy for a purpose like you can be fit for purpose...

All I know is that we are on a quest to find that ultimate in 'health'. Along the way, there are quite a few aspects that will get overlooked simply because they are not sexy enough.

Let's take SLEEP. It's not something that people generally associate with body composition, stress management, strength and gut health, but without optimal amounts, all those systems are compromised. It's also as hard to sort out, if not more so, as nutrition. People just seem to think it's a badge of honour to have less and do more. They get distracted and fall into habits that prevent them from working on this fundamental thing. It's also complicated, as it starts at the beginning of the day! Between the hours of 8 and 12, sunlight hitting the back of the eye stimulates a hormonal cascade that wakes us up fully – a reset button if you like. In the winter months, guess when a lot of people don't see the sunlight? While they are sat at their desks inside. Top tip for today: seek out 10 mins of outside time between 8 and 12... you'll feel infinitely better for it.

This week, HEALTH will be the main underlying topic of the rambles, as many people seek it but get distracted along the way!

Rambles over for a Monday!

#buildthechain

TUESDAY

February 13: Tuesday's rambles… identify a weakness then make it a habit.

I hate weaknesses… the true ones, the ones that you know are there but it's so utterly dull to sort out, but you know you have to. Here are some of mine.

Left shoulder's crap – some issue here whereby every so often something 'goes'.

Left side hip tightness – probably from years of being a national level javelin thrower... something you may not know about me. At school I threw the javelin. At the time, it would have placed me in the top three in university rankings...

Glutes are not weak but other muscles are stronger, and ingrained movement patterns display as weak.

Unable to straighten arm – fully-structural or muscular or just too big biceps.

What can I do about them?

Currently unable to fully sort the hip issue due to the knee, but some work can be done on glutes. What about the hips? Depending on the stretch, I can do a bit more, but have been focusing on the upper body issues.

Upper body wise, I've sought out some therapy on the triceps with our resident chiropractor to scrap my pains away. There's definitely an improvement, but will need to stay on top of this. Regarding the stability issues in the shoulder, I've reverted to basics... every session ends with two shoulder stability and strengthening exercises. Every session begins with scapular retraction and holds – think shoulders back and down (good posture) and hold using various angles and resistance. It's not complicated but the results thus far are:

- No tweaks in the left scapula.
- Fewer neck tweaks. At one stage I was averaging one per month.
- Pushing strength hugely improved, both horizontally and vertically.
- Easier and heavier overhead carries. The overhead position feels more stable.

What has the process taught me? WORK ON MY WEAK-NESSES AND MY STRENGTHS WILL IMPROVE!

Make it a habit, I don't feel like my session has ended now until I've spent 5 mins doing those two exercises. I don't feel ready to train unless I've done those warm-up exercises. Fewer injuries equal more training, which equals more results and faster (as long as you obey the rules of volume and intensity).

Today's rambles: work on those small things holding you back, but first identify the weaknesses and then SEEK HELP. They are weaknesses because you don't know how or can't feel them working. If nutrition is a weakness, seek help. If the mindset is a weakness, talk. You can start now – take a bit of paper and write it all out like I did. Then work on one of those things until it improves.

Rambles... out for a Tuesday,

#buildthechain

WEDNESDAY

February 14

Wednesday's rambles come as a result of two situations that may be applicable to a huge percentage of the population... what do you do training wise when your child is ill? Drum roll, please...

Firstly, in order to fully progress you need to give 100%. If you're tired from no sleep, you're not going to be able to give 100%. The question should be: Will I get something out of this session? Can I match or improve on what I did last time? That's the most important question. If the answer is no, categorically not, then delay the session.

Perhaps you are not sure. Here's another option... take a reload week. Whereas before, your total volume may have been 20 sets per body part of a 15-min amrap (as many reps as possible), you could simply reduce the volume by around a third and thus stay within your recovery curves. Too many people avoid reduced-volume weeks when the shit hits the fan. You will not lose in one week what you have spent months building. The body's

THE PARENT–ING CONUNDRUM

mechanisms are feedback related, and it doesn't like to take major action without having a consistent message for a decent length of time. Strength, body fat, muscle density and muscle fibres are not going to be lost in a week of reducing volume. In fact, it may well stand you in good stead for even faster improvements in the weeks to come.

Secondly, pre-empt the issue by trying to get to bed and sleep earlier. If you know you're going to miss a couple hours in the night, go to bed as early as possible. With a 12-week-old at the moment, for us it's 9.30 lights out and asleep. The completely normal parent may keep going till 11... that's 2.5 hours of extra sleep time engineered through discipline and necessity.

Lastly, if you have to miss training to look after said child completely, it's not the end of the world... get a bodyweight workout in. In 30 mins do as many rounds as possible of:

- 50 air squats
- 50 press-ups
- 50 crunches
- 50 lunges
- 50 burpees

... and I guarantee you'll have a decent movement workout.

I can talk from experience on this one... is it hard not to go #beastmode? YES, but in the long run is it important to take a step back and see the big picture? YES, sometimes #leastmode will get you to your desired location faster and happier!

Rambles out!

THURSDAY

February 15: Thursday rambles – two aspects today, as I couldn't decide.

The law is known as SOD'S LAW.

It had been but one day since I'd posted about working on one's weaknesses and I'd noticed a difference in strength and decreased injury rate. Perhaps might have even mentioned that my good old neck issues hadn't seemed to be bothering me since I'd been taking more care to get regular treatment and worked on some wicked around the area.

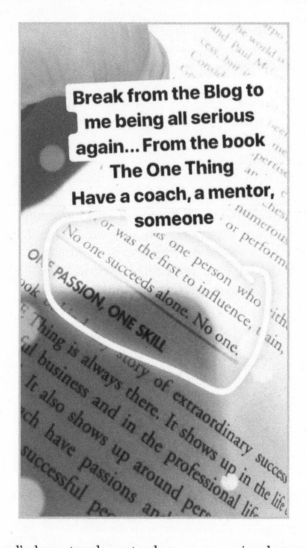

Alas, sod's law struck yesterday, as on a simple warm-up set, I felt that warming session in my right trap... but on the positive, it doesn't appear that it has gone to the same magnitude as previous episodes, so a somewhat small win. I also ceased to continue training, whereas usually I'd just carry on and probably make it worse... yey me! It also shows that while the work I have done has been useful, the underlying reasoning as to why it goes, and/or the origins of why it occurs, need deeper investigation. It is never a finished article... back to the drawing board and enlist some outside help I reckon! Never be afraid to ask for help... as the book 'The One Thing' states.

Most importantly #buildthechain

FRIDAY

February 16

Friday rambles is all about REflection. So, a question: what's gone well this week? If you don't spend time reflecting, I really recommend it!

Have you moved the needle? Have you taken steps towards that outcome goal by continually doing the processes by which you will get there?

For me... yes and no!

On the training front, I've started a new programme and, as with every start of a new programme, the first week is about finding the feet. New rep ranges and rest periods leave a few clues as to where work needs to be done. The thing I've noticed most is that the relative drop-off this week has been higher, meaning that the weights I used for the first set, I've not been able to use for the last set (rep scheme 8/6/4/4/6/8). This has been a long-standing thing of mine that higher rep range, so I'll investigate further. Always seems to be push exercises rather than pull. It's been enjoyable and it's a great programme to work through while I wait for the knee consult.

Nutrition, for me, same as always, consistent to a T.

I've had two members of the gym in for nutrition consultations and started their journeys. Two different people with similar but different goals. Both are starting at slightly different points: one needs flexibility in the day, depending on what happens, the other has a fairly consistent day, so is able to prep in advance easily. Both are hardworking and very consistent with their training, so should be fun to watch their progress towards their goals.

Business, on Thursday SG, decided that we should start vlogging. It's actually been rather amusing to do, and we probably have gained a few followers from it. I can appreciate how these 1 million-follower vloggers enjoy doing what they do. Think next week I'll try and use it to explain who, what and how we train our clients and members, as it will help people on the fence or at the window to make their first step.

What needs working on?

In January I was meticulous about phoning every lead and every person who inquired about the gym. This week it's probably dropped to 85%. We've enjoyed meeting and helping new people, so that will be rectified this coming week as well. New people into our community takes us closer to our goal of impacting the greatest number of people we can in our area, so each person who reaches out we count as a huge opportunity.

That's it – a wee bit of reflection and one thing to work on and rectify, but, as always, the positives are the focus.

How to reflect?

Write down one aspect that has gone well from the following:

- Training
- Nutrition
- Life
- Business

Now pick one thing you could work on and improve.

That's it... simple, but hugely useful!

Rambles out for this week!

On another note, highly recommend listening to Derek Woodske's new podcast EcoBolic Radio – fantastic first one and can't wait for more from him and his guests!

Until next time,

#buildthechain

SATURDAY

February 17: No rambles, just mention of a great pic.

There is an excellent pic in the wonderful book 'Mindset: How You Can Fulfil Your Potential', written by Carol Dweck. The pic compares a GROWTH mindset, where failure is regarded as

an opportunity to grow, and a FIXED mindset, where failure is regarded as the limit of one's abilities. Highly recommend this book to anyone. As I'm out on my morning walk I'm listening to it for the second time, because it brings clarity and learning. It's been one of the most influencing books in the language I'll use with my son, trying to show him the endless possibilities when you adopt a predominantly 'open mindset' where everything is a learning possibility.

Have a great weekend, people, and don't forget to follow us on Instagram @priority6theocmethod.

#buildthechain

MONDAY

February 19

Once you hit your goals, stick around there

Sp Adobe Spark

Monday's rambling comes as a result of my comparison post on Friday.

Friday's post sparked interest in what's going on now that I'm a dad of two, dropped a training day, have less time and sleep isn't as consistent as it was pre-Lillie. There has been a definite mindset switch since having her. Goals have shifted, and in fact, as a result, enjoyment has increased around training. I'm excited as to what direction it will go in after the knee is sorted, but in the meantime I'm thoroughly enjoying the decrease in the overall fatigue that squatting brings. Can you maintain a physique when you're injured? Can you maintain a physique while aspects of your life are not all aligned? I've never been one to compare myself to another person... I take much more from comparing myself to myself, both physically and mentally. As of late, I've done less of the physical comparison (in fact none) and more of the mental, trying to grow my mindset and half the reason for the morning ramblings. I had really no idea where I was at physically in comparison to when I have been at the two lower and upper points in regard to 'weight' in the last three years. Here are the stats:

- Currently sitting at 85.2kg
- Current training days, macros at
  160g protein
  550g CHO
  50g fats
  Caloric intake around 3300, not including cals or macros from veg (can't be bothered with that)
- Non-training day
  160g protein
  220g CHO
  70g fats
  2200 cals

Now training five days a week, four resistance sessions, mostly upper body, except some glute work, and one team WoD (workout of the day) at the weekend with our members for fun and fitness. These have been great to get back into – having tried to do the fitness element by myself on a Saturday, I found it boring and monotonous. Top tip: get yourself to a class format where you train alongside others with the same goals as you!

At one stage, I was on minimal macros, lol, and I was sitting at 77kg. Sixty days later, I was at around 160/300/70, I think (off the top of my head). Was 89kg and didn't feel great about training, even though the size was obviously increasing... that's some rate of gain.

Weird how the body adapts and changes according to its stimulus and intake. Currently, the goal is superhero status for my children, to be an example to our community, and to learn and educate through trying and doing. Most of all, want to enjoy training every time I step onto the gym floor, get the knee sorted and then decide properly on the next fitness path!

Body composition is an interesting one. Do I need to be leaner? Does it bring any extra happiness currently? No, but I wouldn't want to gain any. I'm comfortable with where I'm at... I'm consistent, which is an amazing feeling to know. If I want to, I also know I have the mentality to be able to change a couple things and drop a couple %. With my new higher caloric intake as well, it gives me more room to drop. Instead of 'dieting' at 2500 cals, I can do it at 3000 or 2900 – this wards off hunger. I also can switch foods to make the meals more filling! Have you tried eating over 200g of CHO from a sweet potato?

So, what would be my top tips for people who want to get to the same mentality and happy place?

- Find the training you enjoy that creates the results you want.
- Find a way of eating (and this may require you to learn some fairly basic nutritional knowledge) that allows YOU to have control. That means you are able to measure SOMETHING, i.e. you know how much is going in and going out. If you're not assessing, you are guessing! No solid foundation was ever built on guessing!
- Find people to train with who will keep you turning up.

That's it for this am... quite long actually – #sorry.

And don't forget, #buildthechain

TUESDAY

February 20: Tuesday rambles.

What type of trainer are you? What type of athlete are you? How do you want to be remembered?

These are questions that I think are valuable to people to know the answer to when they train.

In sport there's the naturally talented, who don't work hard, there's the hard worker with average talent, and then there's the talented who work incredibly hard.

Around 15 years old, I was asked one of the questions above. I forget who by, but it pretty much has shaped my thought processes since then.

This applies in any sport, especially at school level, where you are playing for your mates. Here's something I wrote down in a message to myself... I remember doing it before a 'big' game:

'This is who I am... you know if I turn up, I'll work till the last second. You have to beat me, I won't let you win... 100% effort, nothing left, you better bring it'.

That's my mentality in sport, in life, in training. The mentality that if you give everything to it, you put yourself in the best possible place to win, and can't ask any more of yourself other than to then go away and reflect on the performance and develop a plan to improve.

With the CrossFit Open coming up and having watched the last four opens, it's the sort of mentality that could really benefit some athletes. It could help them bring out their best, not to 'beat' others in their gym (that's irrelevant), and not necessarily to qualify for regionals. It's so that they can stand proud, knowing that they gave absolutely EVERYTHING to it. In my view, there is nothing more powerful to one's own mind than that of true 100% effort. Everyone gets enjoyment from different things... I was always driven by effort over the result. I was always taught that, out the effort in, the result will come. I was always praised for effort over the result. It's why I'll never back down, I'll never stop, I'll always respect the effort.

Every night I ask Oscar, 'Tell me something you tried really hard at today.' I'll praise him for that, I'll tell him I'm proud of him for that effort, no matter what it's in. Yesterday he said he tried really hard to get JoJo points (good boy points at school). Today he will probably say he tried really hard at gymnastics. Tomorrow, who knows, but I'll praise his efforts no matter what!

Tuesday rambles out, Build the Chain, share this if it resonates, try it with your kids... it shows them you're interested!

#buildthechain

WEDNESDAY

February 21: Ah, Wednesday rambles!!

Tough one today, as nothing really over the last 24 hours has smashed me in the face as a possible subject.

However, last night the wee man's efforts got him his second gymnastics badge. That's irrelevant really... it's more the fact that for the first time, the gymnastics club has given the parents a termly feedback form. It's simple but what a FANTASTIC idea. Why? Because now I can help him... I know what he needs to be working on. They have identified the weaknesses – the learning opportunities.

Turns out not many gymnastics clubs do this. My niece's doesn't, which I think is a shame, as you don't really know what's going on, quite often can't see, and the kids are too young to relay what they need to work on.

Do you think children should be assessed so young? I don't mind it. He probably isn't even aware, and when I went through it with him, he uttered the words that I was most proud to hear... that he wants to 'do better'. He wants to improve. He sees the older boys doing their flips and twists, and he wants to be able to do them, but he knows he has to turn up and keep trying and eventually he'll get it.

It's funny every club, every sport, every establishment has their own way of doing things. It's probably taken each coach 5 mins to do a form for each kid... But I'll tell you what, it's kept me as a customer, and Oscar and probably Lillie too, for years to come by the fact that they have found an effective way to simply let us know how little OC is doing. In fact, it's also probably sparked an idea for feedback for each of my clients and potentially each of our members. How great would it be that each quarter, everyone got some form of feedback on their progression based on some data and the coaches' perceptions in classes? Potential areas of weakness, identification of strengths and some praise... all positive, all constructive, all extra value. That's the future, I think.

In the meantime, we know it's handstands and cartwheels and upper body strength, and then improvements will come! Let's be honest, which of the above isn't useful in any sport? Strength, agility, multidirectional movements...

Wednesday rambles out!

#buildthechain

THURSDAY

February 22: Thursday Rambles!

Priority

I've always had pride in what I do but never had an ego in the way that I can't learn. All that matters is getting BETTER!

I heard this phrase the other day: 'I've always had pride in what I do but never had an ego in the way that I can't learn. All that matters is getting BETTER!'

I LOVE THIS!

If there's one thing that I love as much as my job (other than my family and friends of course) it's that my job allows me to learn

EVERY single day! It makes me uncomfortable when someone does 'big me up' simply because of the fact that, although I know something about nutrition, exercise and lifestyle, there is more I DON'T know that I DO know!! But it's also the exciting part, the part that keeps me interested. I know enough to help 99.9% of the people on this planet, but I also know that, as I learn more, I will improve that service.

The other amazing thing about the fitness industry is that there are people out there willing to teach you that knowledge, piece by piece. Sometimes, as well, it's not the well-known people... they occasionally have too much invested in a certain way of doing things that pushes them down a certain route. When you teach, you also have the opportunity to learn, whether or not you know what you know as well. If you can actually teach it, you know you know it... there's a tongue tie!

As in the statement above, I have HUGE amounts of pride in what myself, Em and Simon have achieved in bringing Priority 6 and CrossFit Oxford Originals to Abingdon, but I have no ego attached to it. We are constantly seeking improvement, we are constantly upskilling and our team of awesome trainers is constantly evolving and improving their craft.

I'm lucky. If I won the lottery, I'd still turn up to work. That wouldn't change (we may have a second floor and more equipment), but I'd also take five days every month to hire in an 'expert' in a given field and learn from them. We would learn, train, eat, get to know and extract as much information as possible because there is ALWAYS something to learn. There is no ego, just more to learn and more to master, to help that 99.9% we can. That other 0.1% are beyond our scope of practice... all we can do here is refer and let someone with greater knowledge or different skills benefit from our non-ego driven self.

Thursday rambles over #buildthechain

FRIDAY

February 23: OMG ITS FRIDAY!

The REflection day in the morning rambles. So, let's hear it, what's gone well and what's gone in a different direction this week? Where can the improvements be made and, most importantly, what ACTIONS are you proud of and which do you need to take at the weekend and in the week to come?

Training has moved on. I wanted to try the training feedback mechanism I talked about at the end of last week, where three good aspects or three good things from each training session are written down. It has really helped to keep a positive mindset around a programme that doesn't sit in my best rep ranges.

Business has been good. We've been ramping up the interest around the Open, but I'm keen to state that for those not interested in the CrossFit Open, don't worry... you are still very much in the forefront of our programming and ethos. Normal people, achieving exceptional results! However, it's a great way of seeing a community come together, support each other and get work done!

We saw the start of two of our coaches' journeys into the 'Mummy Camp' world. Great to see, and clearly obvious that the market is there in Abingdon for mums who perhaps feel lost with their fitness, and who don't have support in their quest to rediscover themselves through fitness and community. It can be lonely as a mum – interaction is therapy!

So, what about the week to come?

What can be worked on? The main thing actually comes out of the realm of the gym… and more into the parenting realm. I want to spend more time helping Oscar develop his thinking, his key learning skills of reading and writing, his physical ability and his respect. I know he's only four, but foundations are the footing of greatness.

I took 30 mins to learn and apply a subject on Thursday… about the spine. A little bit of Yin to my Yang. It was great. Huge benefits felt, so I will do it again on next Thursday and hopefully reap the rewards!

So how about you… maybe post or write down three things that have gone well in the last seven days. Next, find something you are keen to improve over the next seven days. Then, don't stop there, identify the processes and write them out. Write them in a diary and take ACTION. Daily action is the key to consistency, which is the key to your RESULTS.

REflection is powerful… reflection sets you up for a wonderful day.

Happy Friday people. Last ramble of the week… hands were frozen but the dream is closer.

#buildthechain

SATURDAY

February 24: No rambles today, just Open-related news!

So much excitement, so many nerves, so much support…
    The Open comes around each year, and every year the excitement builds as people get to compare their best efforts to the

top in the world. It makes you appreciate how good they are, even when this would be just a part of their training ramp-up to the Games. Nonetheless, it gives us a chance at a gym to build on the community, to bring people together and use fitness as our guide! Top first efforts from everyone. I even gave it a go myself after over two years' absence from anything that could be construed as cardio, and guess what? We went live, I could feel the support, I enjoyed it and I can't wait to scale the rest of it.

MONDAY

February 26: Monday rambles!

A question to start the week... If you could go back in time and give your 14-year-old self some advice, what would it be? For me, there are a few things.

- Start building your body now. I started training or thinking about fitness at 16/17. The confidence I gained from it was unparalleled. I saw improvements in my body and it ricocheted into other areas of life. I got better at sport, I got better at work, I got better at talking to girls, all through the fact that I was building my body strength and taking control. If only I'd started that two or three years earlier!

- Read more. Read about significant leaders, about successful people, about business and self-improvement. So many answers and questions have come from reading these books. Skills I never learnt at school, I've found in these books.

Ok, it's minus 2.5 and I can't type anymore.

There's more to come, but maybe tomorrow!

If you could give your 14-year-old self two pieces of advice, what would they be?

Rambles out...
Don't forget...

#buildthechain

TUESDAY

February 27

Right, Tuesday rambles. Now, currently it's minus four according to Instagram, so this one is telling, thought-provoking, and more... just do it!

Two simple pieces of advice that will probably do more for your health than anything else this year!

1. Chew your food! Genuinely, we rush our food and don't give it enough time to start the breakdown process in our mouth, leading to a host of issues further on in the gut!

The more you chew, the less the gut has to do, the quicker the release of energy to your systems and the faster your gut microbiome can do its job!

2. Sleep from 10–6. There is a multitude of excuses why people 'can't do this'. Most are bullshit, and just as many are due to lack of organisation and time-wasting earlier in the day. Deal with that, then you will see your eight hours! Get up at 5am... go to bed at 9pm. Prioritise your sleep. Get into a routine. Turn off Netflix, the TV. Record the programme and get to bed! It's amazing how many people suffer from only five hours sleep... it's what I've always done. You do it because you got into a crappy habit at school or university and it's hard to change a habit! Sometimes you have to go

through that to come out the other side healthier, more recovered and more energetic!

Simple, but here's the issue: people don't like simple, they like complex and special. Not today... get the simple shizzle right consistently, and then I'll give you the magic after that!

Tuesday out... #buildthechain

WEDNESDAY

February 28: Wednesday rambles... The importance of Yin!

We live a life of Yang – everything is action, everything is speed, everything is pressured. Today's rambles aren't on what effect that has on us mentally or hormonally, but more on what we can do to counteract the negatives of all that Yang!

Firstly, I am a massive fan of soft tissue work, especially post my first CrossFit workout in a long, long time! I'm lazy when it comes to Yin work, and so as much as possible I will get someone else to do the restoration for me. I know how physical it is to be a therapist... I am one (not many people know that). I've treated American footballers and someone who now plays at Leicester City FC. At some stage in the future, I'll probably incorporate therapy back into my client's training, to release locked muscle tension. We are, however, really lucky to have some fantastic therapists at our gym, each with their own slightly different skills and approaches. You always feel better in the days after getting treated... there's the initial blood flow to tied-up areas, and then there's the settling down of those tissues. It's time really well spent in my eyes, especially as I can relax into it.

The second Yin that I've used in tough times is Headspace. I love it! I've tried other apps, but none allow me to sink into relaxation so easily as that one. I can feel the benefit of the slowed breathing and the ability to hear my own thoughts. In a world where I'm constantly being talked to, those 10–15 mins can feel like hours.

So, tips for today:

- Get a great practitioner to work on you. Don't settle on the first one... try a few out to see what quality is out there. I'll tell you now, they differ HUGELY! Find the one who listens to your needs and assesses and treats the pain and potential causes.
- Download Headspace and take the 10-day challenge. If you aren't sold after 10 days of trying it, genuinely, you may have

an issue and might need some other guided mindset tuition. It's not happy, it's not weak... it's sensible in an era of information overload, extreme demand and constant pressures.

That's Wednesday out... less wind today, so wasn't crying while typing! I need your help though! Facebook has changed its timeline. Basically, unless you comment and unless you share on Facebook, these rambles won't get seen. Upsetting for me, as the aim is always to help as many as possible, but don't need to resonate with more than one to make it worthwhile. However, if you share and if you comment, Facebook will essentially see this as something that people want to see in their timelines. So please share, like and comment for me!

#buildthechain

THURSDAY

March 1: Thursday rambles.
Firstly, snow in the eyes!

Secondly 'the sweet spot'. I've been thinking recently about the three aspects of the gym – the three most common reasons why people come and how they intertwine. They are:

- Aesthetics
- Performance
- Health

Taking each one to the extreme leaves the others null and void. For example, performance... if you take it to the extreme, what do you find?

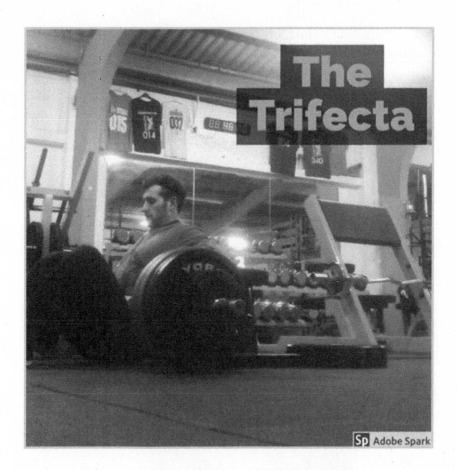

The Trifecta

Sp Adobe Spark

Health drops. Injuries are more prevalent. Blood markers indicate inflammation and potentially irreversible damage. Aesthetics change (while for the individual this is obvious, for the mainstream this quite often veers away from the 10% for males' sweet spot of body fat, a massive generalisation but it's close).

Aim for optimal health, and performance will probably not be as high as it could be.

To aim for aesthetics in the way bodybuilders do is to take aesthetics to the extreme, and performance and health markers will decrease.

So, where's the sweet spot? It's a blend of all of these. It also changes over time, with age, with goals to a certain degree, and with phases of training. People, I think, get dragged into one of these areas more than others, especially when there isn't a clear vision.

There's a fine balance... one that's worth looking for. That's it for today – too cold!

#buildthechain

MONDAY

March 5: Monday rambles.

Well, it feels nice to be doing this in plus temperatures rather than minus and snowing!

Two things this am to discuss. There's a phrase I like that I heard recently which goes along with another phrase that I wholeheartedly believe in:

'Life happens FOR you, not TO you'.

It's in the same vein as 'everything happens for a reason'.

In the world of fitness, it could be an injury… it's a reminder that something wasn't optimal. You were doing something that didn't match your body's mechanics, you didn't listen to the signals, your body's shown a weakness that needed working on, as the demand placed on it caused trauma. But guess what? You come back more knowledgeable, with more tools in the shed and stronger than before! At least that's the way I view it currently. I say currently because everyone has a tipping point. In terms of injuries, the ones I have had are, in comparison to some, minor. I don't know how I would deal with something major. Hopefully, I'll never find out.

In other aspects of life, I heard a story about 'little Eddie – he's shy and he's great at baseball'. That's how Eddie was introduced as a child. When Eddie hit 19, he got a major injury on his way to becoming a pro. Eddie was now just 'little Eddie – he's shy'… what am I getting at? Be careful what identity you attach to someone. Imagine that person… he's now lost the fact that he's great at baseball and it's now ingrained in his personality that he is a) small and b) shy. This guy eventually found his true calling and is now a well-respected entrepreneur, but how many others never find that calling? I can fully relate to that guy. All through school and well into adult life, I attached my identity to a sport. When the sport went, what was I? WHO was I? If you have kids, I think the goal is to promote values and principles and let them decide WHO they are… At the moment, it's a cave explorer – in years to come, who knows?

I'm currently also working on the:

Build the Chain Diary

... a written diary that will help you collect your positivity, keep your accountability, focus your thoughts. So far, it's an idea... who knows what it will materialise into!

#buildthechain #enjoyyourday

TUESDAY

March 6

Tuesday rambles... choice bias in the fitness industry. One of the things about the fitness industry is that people tend to navigate to the answer that they want to hear, the one that doesn't challenge their belief system. The path of least resistance and the one that reassures them that it is the right path.

Nutrition is an easy one to use as an example. Most people will look for someone who seems to have the same sort of belief that they do, when perhaps a drastic overhaul is necessary. As a coach, when I came into the industry there was a huge movement towards a Paleo approach to nutrition. It's not by any means a bad option and is founded on great principles, but it did pigeonhole a lot of nutritional advisers. Nowadays, the movement seems to be back towards a more science-based, measured approach, not shaming any foods. I'm sure in the future the balance will swing again. Nutrition is a funny one, as all nutritional strategies could take you to your goal, maybe not optimally, but each has its merits and each could work. It's about finding the one that resonates. That's why we have many different approaches to our nutritional strategies, rather than hanging our hat on one strategy. There are, however, times when the goal dictates the approach. A huge percentage of participants will need a more science-based approach. There will be some who can intuitively eat the right things at the right times in the right amounts, but they tend to be outliers and/or knowledgeable enough to make information-based choices... they ain't guessing!

Training wise, again people tend to navigate towards a type of training that suits their psyche at the time. I'll be the first to admit that my motivation for training is to lift things, but I am fully aware that probably a lot of benefits could come from more movement-based 'Yin' activities. In fact, this weekend I head down to Bath to a 10-year mentorship meet-up at Body Development. Tom has a blend of 'Yang' and 'Yin' based techniques, so it will be interesting to see some of those and what others have incorporated in the last 10 years.

Today, look into something that challenges your beliefs if different from what you believe... perhaps the Flat Earth Society, perhaps Vegan nutrition. What can you learn from someone else's perspective?

#buildthechain

Wednesday

March 7: Wednesday rambles...
Flat as a pancake!

Today's ramblings come after listening to two coaches, who I admire and respect, discussing strength, life, business and shizzle on a relatively new podcast owned by Derek Woodske. We all get times when training just isn't going right... the days where you just couldn't post anything on social media because it's so uninspiring there just isn't any point. Social media is a wonderful highlight reel of amazing things. It can be used for:

- Business, to get your word out there and deliver quality content to people who may never have met you.
- It's a fantastic way to advertise your ethos and your mission to the world.
- It's hugely motivational to see what people are capable of doing.
- It's great for keeping in touch with your friends.
- It's great for creating a tribe of people with a common purpose.
- It's a great learning tool.
- It can also be fun.

But in the same breath, it can be the exact opposite of all those things.

So, on the days when you do feel flat, when motivation wanes, when you can't be bothered... what do you do?

First of all, notice it! Personally, I know it's a phase – I've been through enough of them before. This week in training, for example, the lifts have stalled, and there's been zero progress, if anything a regression of some weights. So what am I going to do about it?

Two things.

Firstly, I'm not going to feel sorry for myself. As the CrossFit Invictus motto goes, 'I am the master of my fate, I am the captain of my soul'. Basically, it's within me to change!

Secondly, I'm going to look at the reasons why training isn't going particularly well. All aspects – life, business, sleep, family, stressors, etc – will be examined to see where training currently sits in the hierarchy. If it's not top or close to the top, then I'm not going to push for the social media highlight reel shots. I'm going to accept that it's on the back burner, ticking over. It will come back, but for some reason, I need energy in other areas, and that's FINE! Of course, if I'm just being a lazy sh1t and making excuses, I'll call myself out on that and sort it. I'm my own biggest critic, so I'm comfortable with challenging my own performance.

If you're after a change, you need to move the needle, and you need to make something more important... move it up the hierarchy of importance. Establish that and you'll see where your motivation lies.

Wednesday's out
#buildthechain

THURSDAY

March 8: Thursday rambles.

There is no standing still on the path to your goal. You are either taking a step forwards or taking a step back. Each action you perform is taking you either closer or further away. The aggregation of marginal gains will always lead to AN outcome... which one is entirely down to the habits you have or the discipline in your action.

Take time to create POSITIVE ACTION on your path. As an example, here are the habits I have instilled. They are so ingrained that people would probably question what was wrong if I didn't do them:

- Wake early, always before 6.
- Go to sleep before 10.
- Train.
- Eat a diet based on plants and meat... not derivatives of, but the actual living element.
  (and now to a certain extent, write the daily rambles)

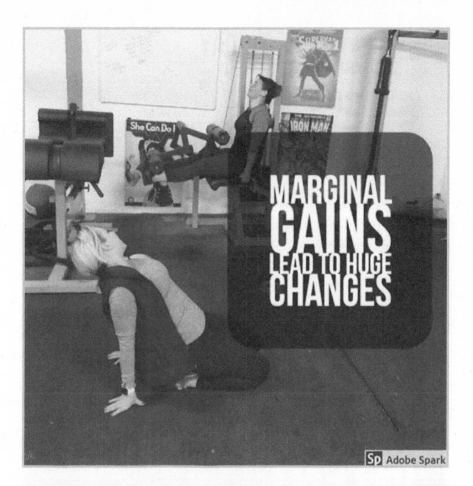

Those are some of my habits – they are positive. They have allowed me to achieve a structure that lets me work on my passions... family, our business, my physical body, the ability to help others avoid the pitfall and mistakes I made along the way.

Create positive habits, and the old negative ones will disappear.

End of Thursday rambles,
#buildthechain

FRIDAY

March 9

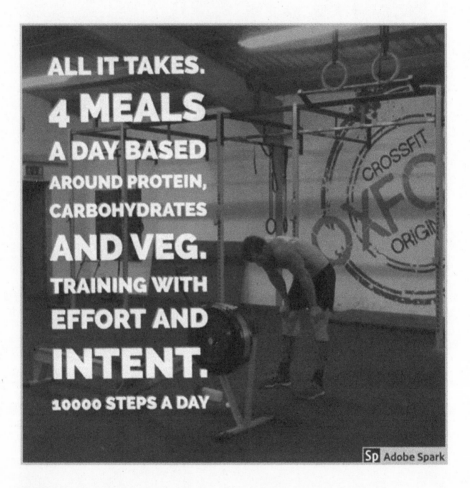

F riday rambles – we revisit our hashtags meaning… the concept of Building the Chain.

It's a great way to stay on the right track, and this theme is used by our gym to hold you accountable to yourself and keep you on track.

THE MORNING RAMBLINGS ⌒ 127

It all starts with your goals, your outcome goals. Write them out:

- Lose 20lbs, for example.

Now, you actually have little control over the number. You can't say for sure how long it will take and whether that figure will make you happy.

But what you do next WILL have an effect on your life for the positive – you will feel happier and more in control of your life.

Write out the habits and processes by which you need to maintain daily that will get you to your goal.

Eat four meals a day consisting of lean protein, carbohydrates from XYZ sources, and two to three servings of veg, etc. Easily definable and easy to say whether you achieved or didn't.

Go to the gym three days a week (preferably to a class or scheduled coached session... research shows you train harder and get better results).

Hit 10,000 steps a day.

Introduce three daily habits that will build confidence, that are easy to quantify and that are habits for a lifetime.

Now buy either a wall poster or a book of a whole calendar year. Have your habits written out above it and stick it up on the wall.

Each day you do the processes by which you achieve your goals, put a BIG green X through the day. Right now, it should be easy to hit those Xs. Your aim is to NOT BREAK THE HABIT CHAIN!

The habit chain is a powerful concept – it puts you in charge and gives you a visual representation of your commitment to yourself. Do you really want to break that chain? I guarantee that once you see 10 days in a row of big GREEN Xs, you're going to think twice about unbooking that class or choosing takeaway over your nutrition plan. Ask yourself, DO YOU REALLY WANT TO BREAK THE HABIT CHAIN? It's powerful because it hands YOU the CHOICE to make or break your goal in a visual and easy to see way!

'But Ollie, what happens if I do succumb and the chain is broken?' Simple – you write the number of days you managed to chain together in the day you go to... Then you call or message your coach and then you identify why... Then you, here's the important part, MOVE ON and try to better the chain... beat your last run. You are not a bad person for having a slip-up, but what you do after defines your personality and commitment to what you want to achieve. Those who achieve greatness and their ambitions are those who see that slip-up, learn from it and move on. What if you are not currently being coached by a coach? Simple – reach out. All you have to do is contact and I will try where I can to help you through the issue.

Go out, buy a wall chart and let's see who can have the longest habit chain...

I guarantee that the person with the longest chain will be the person with the greatest results!

#buildthechain
All it takes... is for you to #buildthechain

MONDAY

March 12

No rambles today... helping mother and father move house. So, there's the ramble – when family calls, give help...

#buildthechain

TUESDAY

March 13: Tuesday rambles!

So, Saturday after team WoD I nipped off down to Bath. I went to a mentorship 10-year anniversary at Body Development. I think I did my first course with Tom there about six or seven years ago (I think it was a Fat Loss Weekend) and regularly attended for a couple years, so I haven't been back there for a few years now. Firstly, there's my first mistake!

This gym and Tom were the inspiration to me wanting to set up and own my first gym. I remember talking with Tom on the phone as I sat in April Cottage as he gave up his time to talk me through the finances of what I would need to set up and run a gym. I still have the notes on Evernote now.

The gym has changed a lot since I was last down… the ability to practise movement, but still blending it with strength and speed. What use is a strength if you can't display it? There is obviously a lot of care and knowledge to the programming in order to hit all movement planes. The basics of human movement are at the heart of everything.

In the world of fitness, you can become very insular in the way you do things. When you step out of your gym and your way of doing things, you see how much variety can be added. I'm not saying I'll take everything I saw on Saturday and run with it. I'm saying that everything is worth exploring and learning about. It keeps the game interesting and fresh.

In my own training, I shall be adopting some of what I learnt on the day, as it's highlighted huge holes in my own athletic development and would reduce injury rate for certain.

What's the message of today… seek out mentors, seek out those more knowledgeable than you. Learn from them, don't copy but learn the reasons, learn the principles and then develop your own path of doing things. We've developed our own path at P6… a great way of doing things. But we wouldn't be the gym we are and we wouldn't remain at the forefront of fitness and health if we stopped improving and stopped evolving.

#buildthechain

WEDNESDAY

March 14

YOU CAN ONLY EVER GUARANTEE YOUR EFFORT

"Take a lyre player: he's relaxed when he performs alone, but put him in front of an audience, and it's a different story, no matter how beautiful his voice or how well he plays the instrument.

Why? Because he not only wants to perform well, he wants to be well received – and the latter lies outside his control."

———

EPICTETUS

Wednesday rambles after seeing a quote from the Greek philosopher Epictetus. It talks about how people perform differently when alone or when in front of an audience. A perfect example of concentrating on being the best version of yourself... the player cannot influence how their craft is received. They just play to the best of their ability.

I've always had a theory: perform to 100% of your effort and ability – if it's enough, you win, if it isn't, next time come back 'stronger'. That's it, that's my thought process in sport, in exams, in anything. It's why the result of something, especially a sporting endeavour, was never about the celebration or the disappointment. No, it was when I reflect on the game – did I put it all in? Did I empty the tank, did I chase everything, did I make the right decision at the right time? Could I have played better and done my job better for the team? Its why I also don't agree with the 'there's no I in team' saying. There is... we each have a responsibility to the team to perform at our highest effort... you have to take care of your own effort for the team to function. Those who disagree with that are scared of self-evaluating their own effort. If each individual performs their individual jobs to the best of their ability and with the most amount of effort, then the team will play well, as they will play as a team (as that's part of the individual's job, to play the role they have been coached to do). Teammates can enhance your effort by their presence, but they can't do your job for you.

Concentrate on effort. Take care of that, then the result will be what it will be. If you're good enough, you win, if you're not... reflect, identify, plan and take ACTION. Next time put in the effort again and the results may be more favourable, but your reflection will be the same...

Wednesday rambles... out,
#buildthechain

THURSDAY

March 15

Right, rambles this Thursday are short and sweet, as it's peeing down with rain.

Adobe Spark

Most of us nutritionally have a nutritional range of 17 foods... 17!!!! Your gut suffers from this! This limited exposure to foods limits your health and limits the range of nutrients available to you.

Recently, at a mentorship weekend at Body Development in Bath, Pete Williams used a great analogy of the gut. Taking in a greater variety of foods gives your gut the variety of a rainforest in terms of its bacteria and resistance. If one plant contracts a disease, another will take its place and fill the void. If you limit your foods, the gut is like that of a cornfield... one disease and the whole crop is wiped out. The soil is ruined and you can't grow and recover from it...

The challenge: write down all the nutrient-dense foods you currently eat. Your aim next week is to increase that by five foods.

('Nutrient dense' means anything in its natural state, so things like chocolate, prepared foods and the like don't count.)

Rambles out. Try the challenge... if you want, list your foods below!

#buildthechain

FRIDAY

March 16: It's REflection Friday!

This week has been a bit of a mental one, probably due to a trip down to Bath and a trip to help move my parents. It's all been a bit rushed. However, it's been a solid week of training, it's been a solid week of business, and those kiddies are keeping us on our toes, that's for sure!

Training has been thought-provoking since the weekend. There's definitely been a shift of thought process in what I want to achieve from my training currently... a movement towards resetting goals, re-establishing certain movements that I can't currently do, as I've neglected certain modalities. I will have to work on some fundamental weaknesses, which will probably be tedious to overcome, but I'll draw on the expertise around me to help with that. You are the sum of the five people you spend the most time with. Lucky for me, those five are talented and passionate about what they do! Long term, I think I'll incorporate some of these measures into all my client's programming too... I'm not talking overhaul, I'm talking appreciation for things that are often forgotten. I think too that the benefits of group training in my own training has been lost for some time, so potentially opening up my

REFLECTION FRIDAY

own training times for people to join in may increase results... we shall see.

Business has seen a marked increase in enquiries. I think this is because we are getting better at putting the message out there, and because we are showing that anyone can slot into our workouts. Again, the common theme coming through the telephone conversations is that of wanting to BELONG to something. It probably comes down to the main human need for appreciation. We appreciate every member as they spread our message.

Isn't it amazing how kids develop? I'm lucky I have two gorgeous ones. Seeing the interaction of one with the other... Lillie looks for Oscar, he makes her smile... Oscar full of love wants to 'huggy' his baby sister. It's also, on reflection, plain to see the need for attention for both. When O acts up, it seems as though it's a lack of attention from the person he wants attention from that sparks a reaction need, e.g. getting up at suppertime. It's interesting that, again, the fundamental need for attention and appreciation is a key driver in behaviour.

So grateful for this week...

- I'm grateful that an old mentor has given me a new perspective and some fun ways to train my weaknesses.
- I'm grateful for the family I have.
- I'm grateful for having the opportunities to change the trajectory of someone's thoughts.

What could I work on next week?... the list is endless.

#buildthechain

MONDAY

March 19

It's Monday... snow still here... how on earth is it the start of British Summertime in about six days' time?!?!

Righty, onto the rambles...

The art of taking action. A lot of us live in a false reality, one where we believe in our thoughts and the stuff that happens in our heads, rather than the reality of our ACTIONS.

Anyone can say that they are going to do something, whether it's losing weight, sticking to their nutrition, training hard, turning up, etc, but it's only when they repeat the necessary actions enough times do they truly benefit. They perform the action in their alternative reality... that's useless. When they actually physically take action, when they can prove to themselves they

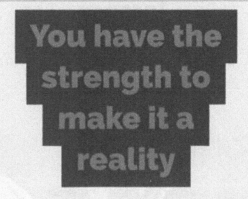

You have the
strength to
make it a
reality

"You have to assemble your life yourself,
action by action."

———

MARCUS AURELIUS

dailystoic.com

Sp Adobe Spark

turned up, they put in the effort and they take the desired steps, then the goal moves into reality.

Take the action now to stop creating that false you in your head. Instead, create that person in the actual physical world, the one where you will see the benefits of it.

Anyone can create a vision in their heads, but the ones who make it there are the ones who take the necessary steps to get there!

#buildthechain

TUESDAY

*March 20: Tuesday rambles is about 'demanding
the best from yourself'.*

Set your mind to something... make this the focus of your existence and set up everything you need to achieve it.

Quite often, the difference between achieving and failing (also
known as 'learning') is one wrong decision, one wrong move, a
meal out, a missed training session, an illness. Why is it that these
single events completely derail you from your desired outcome?

Two reasons to mull over today:

1. You didn't want it badly enough.
2. You didn't know how to achieve it because you didn't get
    everything in place to succeed.

I am a huge believer in the first one of these. I believe that anyone
has the capacity to achieve what is on their mind, both realistically
and otherwise. I say that because it's been seen time and time again
that people have defied the odds and achieved far more than they

dreamed of! Now I say this to keep it simple: ALL YOU NEED IS TO WANT IT MORE THAN YOU WANT SOMETHING ELSE. Then, you *will* achieve it. When you actually WANT something on such a deep level that nothing else will get in the way, you *will* achieve it. If there's something nagging at you telling you to quit or to give in, and you do... then the prize wasn't big enough, and you didn't fail through lack of motivation, you failed because you didn't truly want it. It's a tough pill to swallow, but I think it's a valid way of thinking about things. Essentially, you spread yourself too thin, and the pulls of other areas were greater than the pull of your goal.

#buildthechain

WEDNESDAY

March 21: Wednesday rambles! Hopefully, I'll get this one out in the morning!

I want to talk about the invisible existence you live in. There are so many people in the world... you are one of them, yet you often care more about what those others think about you than how you think about yourself. You take actions based on what you perceive others think of you. It's so screwed up really.

Here's a suggestion:

- Do it for you.

Here is my training and health history:

- Youth – trained for sport, for me, I loved competing. Happy OC.
- I trained for vanity, for me, I wanted to look good. Happy OC.

- I trained for CF, for me... to compete. Happy OC.
- I trained for business, not for me. Unhappy, miserable a-hole OC.

Back training for me, to enjoy the variety of training and to eventually be able to train with my son and daughter (although wifey will still be able to run faster than I will). For me, this will bring enjoyment...

When you start on your fitness and health journey, ask yourself: is this for me, or is it for someone else?... It can have carried over into both, but make sure that the lion's share is for YOU.

#buildthechain

THURSDAY

March 22

The worry factor... I had a conversation yesterday about 'worry-ing'. It had never occurred to me until then that people worry in different ways.

As with everything, the types of worry below are probably depend-ent on the subject, as different things stress people differently.

Some worry at the prospect of something... an event that builds or is in the back of their mind such that the perceived outcome causes worry.

I myself most of the time don't worry in advance... why? Because it hasn't happened yet. In my head, I can't worry about something that hasn't happened... I can give it thought and prepare for an outcome, but I don't worry about it. I think it's also a learnt trait. I'm fairly sure it's come from the years of self-help books, and listening to people I consider knowledgeable and truthful. I think of it as 'wasted' energy TO ME. That's not to say that worrying is a bad thing, and I completely get that people's worries are valid. I just choose now to concentrate my energy on influencing the outcome, rather than worrying about the possibility that something might or might not happen.

I'm sure there is an extraordinary amount of people who put off coming down to the gym because they are worried about X, Y or Z that hasn't happened yet. They are putting on hold their hopes and dreams because of the prospect of something bad happening that might (or in our case won't) never happen. In fact, it's going to give that person the confidence and motivation to improve ALL aspects of their life.

Be the person who thinks differently today... maybe take on a different perspective, look at things differently and challenge your thoughts!

#buildthechain

FRIDAY

March 23: Today's ramble is, of course,
Reflection Friday.

It's been a week of progress, it's been a moving-forward week, it's been a step in the right direction... but for me, in all honesty, I could have given more. Next week will see the return of a few

"It never ceases to amaze me: we all love ourselves more than other people, but care more about their opinion than our own."

———

MARCUS AURELIUS

dailystoic.com

daily rituals that will help to dial in the concentration into the most important areas.

I'm a big fan of to-do lists but think I can eek more from them by changing them to action lists.

To-do lists can have the gratification of ticking things off, but they tend to end up being loaded with unimportant tasks, rather than with things that will create massive change and big leaps forwards. Basically, they become lists of things to keep you busy rather than effective!

When I look back on the week, I see certain performance markers that are measurable, like a training diary... you can see progress. Like weight on the scales... you have a performance marker. Like body fat % and pictures... you have performance markers. Combined, these performance markers show the big picture and what needs to be tweaked in order to head closer to the results you want. We've definitely moved forwards, but the magnitude hasn't been big enough for my liking.

Training has been fun this week... a change in programming, not feeling so beaten up by the large volumes, and the inclusion of a bit of gymnastic work and a new warm-up routine have been positive. For my clients, it always astounds me when crunch time comes how people always outperform their targets. We set specific and measurable targets, realistic ones, and often they get smashed. Confidence and motivation come from seeing success, but results come from continuous striving for positive progress and a deeper understanding of why your goals matter!

Business has been good this week, more specifically the community side of the Open. The coming together of people to support, cheer, encourage and engage with one another over something so simple as adult PE. It's amazing the confidence and motivation that can come from a voice shouting your name with that tone that just says 'we are here, we want you to succeed'. At times in life, you get people not wanting you to succeed. They want you to fall flat on your face because it makes them feel better about their lack of progress and their inability to commit to change and a goal. Those people haven't experienced what it is like to have someone fully back them and fully encourage them. Those are the people who need to experience our gym, our ethos and our members. From the first to the last finisher, you are all better humans than you were yesterday, because you have all taken steps towards a stronger, healthier you!

On the family front, I think I asked at some point this week whether it was 'too late to put her back from where she came'. It's amazing what a disruption in sleep can do to you. That, combined with a couple days of grizzles, and you quite often question what you were thinking! I wouldn't change the little cutie in any way, that's what. It's funny because, through all the crying, that one smile comes out and instantly your mindset changes. there's a lot to be said for that... one smile and your mindset and perspective change. Maybe we should just smile and laugh more often? In the hard times, seek a smile. When you get one, hold onto it... it will probably see you through the next 20 mins of crying. With end of term coming up and little OC being around for the holidays, has anyone got any good ideas of activities for the day? We've booked him into one full gymnastics fun day. Anyone else ship their kids off for the day? Has to be active – perhaps a marathon for 4-year-olds?

Next week:

- To-do lists and how to tweak them.
- Decision making.

Have a great Friday, relax, reflect on the week, seek improvement not perfection, and remember why you started!

#buildthechain

MONDAY

March 26: When you don't have time... build a bodyweight habit.

Firstly... damn the clock change! I was enjoying not having to walk in the dark in the mornings. It's amazing what a bit of light in the morning does to your mood and wellbeing! Anyway, Monday rambles...

Let's talk about breaking it down into habits. I was re-listening to something I had listened to in the new year about habits and building them... after all, building the chain is all about

habit building. Sometimes I think people aim too high too soon, when in actual fact they needn't aim for that finished article right away. What would be more effective is to take the low-hanging fruit in the meantime and roll with that first.

For example, someone's goals might be:

- Get stronger
- Lose weight
- Feel more energetic

Within these goals, they might have specifics of:

- Add 20kg to their squat, deadlift and bench press, or they might just simply want to be able to lift their child without feeling as though they are going to put their back out!

- They might want to lose 5kg to look good on holiday, or they might want to lose 50kg to completely change their life.
- They may be hooked on junk food and wake up with no energy, or they may sit at a desk all day and feel like they have lost their get-up-and-go, so they decide to eat perfectly from the get-go. For males, a sure-fire way to know if your hormones and energy are balanced is that each morning you wake up ready to go, if you know what I mean.

Anyway, as the way to get there, people will quite often set these sorts of habit:

- I'm going to go to the gym three times a week for an hour.
- I'm going to eat perfectly.
- I'm not going to drink until my holiday.

While these are fantastic and great final habits to achieve from the outset, MOST people will only keep these up for a limited time if they jump right in without analysing if they're actually doable.

Common themes I hear are: 'I didn't have the time to train' or 'The nutrition was too hard and took up too much time' or 'I missed one day and then couldn't get back on track'.

So, what's my advice for someone?... Go for the low-hanging fruit.

If you are short of time, aim for one workout a week at the gym at the most suitable time. It still means that you might have to sacrifice something, but if you watch one episode on Netflix every night, then you DO have time... you are just lying to yourself. Use that one training session to LEARN. If your gym is set up like ours, you will be coached each session. Grab the instructor at the end if they have time, and ask for five bodyweight exercises and five kettlebell exercises that you could do at home. Here are my five:

- Press-ups
- Squats
- Lunges
- Planks
- Crunches

Within those five exercises are probably hundreds of progressions and regressions to make them harder or easier – YouTube them.

From there, your aim now is not to do three-hour long sessions at the gym in the week, but to maintain a daily habit of 15 mins a day working through those five bodyweight exercises. If you are starting from no exercise, then 15 mins for five days a week is better than three half-arsed gym sessions that you only do for one week because 'you don't have time'. You're more likely to hit 15 mins daily than do three 60-min sessions.

When you can manage five 15-min sessions (or even seven), increase the time to 20 mins. Keep doing that and your goal of increased strength will become a reality and your goal of weight loss will happen.

That's it for today... I'll try to remember to post tomorrow how you could progress nutrition over time too, but the mind wanders and I'll prob end up in a different thought direction tomorrow. Remember, you don't always have to aim to hit the end goal on the first day... build the habits, Build the Chain and eek what you can from each stage of development, and the process will be viewed in a different light!

If you want to know where to get some kettlebells from, drop me a message and I'll advise.

Have a great week... #buildthechain

WEDNESDAY

March 28: Wednesday rambles a go!

The KISS programme.
The 'Keep It Stupid Simple' programme.
This year I've come to the conclusion that keeping a fitness and nutrition regime as simple as possible, whilst completely

unsaleable, is probably the most effective and sustainable way to hit your goals.

Here are the main principles:

Training: hit each body part three times a week. Get out of breath at least once in the day.

Nutrition: eat a wide variety of foods from a list of foods that are nutrient dense and don't cause inflammation (to you). Keep protein and carbs to before and after workouts. The other meals should consist of protein and veg, and add some fats (not too much, as it could easily take you over your calorie requirements).

Sleep: sleep like you train... focus as much intensity on your sleep ritual as you do on your training.

Activity: get a Fitbit and track your steps. Aim to go 2000 more than you've currently been doing, until you hit at least 10000... ideally more.

Mindset: study the art of stressing less and creating meaningful relationships. You don't need many friends if the ones you have are true ones.

Poor accountability and planning are the two main reasons why I think people 'fail' on programmes. A clear vision sets the standard for where you are going. Once the vision or plan is clear, it's easy to then understand where things are going well and what needs attention.

Around 80% of people could do the above and live a more confident, happy life. The other 20% are crazy people who need more direction and more planning out... they need more in order to achieve more. Their goals are perhaps more specific, or they have shifted more emphasis in their lives towards their leisure goals or performance-oriented ones. Usually they have been through an extended KISS programme and are now searching for more.

Key principle for today: Keep It Stupid Simple for as long as possible. Get the most out of the least, and you will end up exceeding by far your original targets.

As always, #buildthechain

THURSDAY

March 29: Listen!

You learn something every day!
Recently, I've been doing A LOT of nutrition consults. Seems as though people are getting into the holiday season and want to tidy everything up so that they feel a little bit more confident on

the beach come the summer. So, they are giving themselves a good amount of time to adjust their diets.

Well, yesterday I relearned a valuable lesson... listen, don't talk!

I won't name names, but a client came in and we discussed their nutrition in broad terms of getting a bit leaner. They eat well during the week so they can eat a bit of junk food at the weekend. They are probably in a deficit during the week while they train. The client didn't train at the weekend, but had allowed themselves sufficient leeway to be able to start the process again on Monday at the same weight as the week before. Sounded simple enough... start with some small changes and educate over the course of time, so that we fuel training and reduce on days of less activity. We talked for about 50 mins about structuring the week, planning meals and fuelling training. I then asked a question I should have asked at the beginning of the session, and just sat back and listened...

'So this junk food at the weekend... take me through a typical day.'

What happened next had me in giggles for about 10 mins, more since it was completely unexpected because of the weekday nutrition regime and also because the person is in pretty good nick. Luckily, as well, they saw the humour in it too, otherwise they could have been offended.

'Well it usually starts with me getting a box of a dozen Krispy Kremes... it takes me about an hour, but I eat those first...'

'I'm sorry, come again? You eat all 12???'

'Yep, it's quite easy now... it takes about an hour.'

[Insert OC laughter and amazement]

I think my next words were:

'I don't know whether I'm impressed or amazed by that.'

Anyway, the moral of the story is: a) ask the right questions, and b) shut up and listen.

#buildthechain

SATURDAY

*March 31: Reflection Fridays but I forgot to post,
so it's coming Saturday!*

So, what's the week been like for you? With the end of the CrossFit Open on Monday, there's been an excitement at final placings and the comparison with last year. It's plain to see as a coach the VAST improvement in our athletes. At our gym, we try to help people improve their performance exponentially and help them exceed

their own expectation, but we also value health and longevity. This year it was easy to see that the guys and girls were physically looking stronger, more confident and doing it with a nervous smile on their faces! It's easy to see the excitement of the Open will be missed!

For myself the Open has defiantly brought back the need to get out of breath, the lungs burning and floor lying. It's made me look at my own training and re-evaluate what I want from it.

P6 has been abuzz this week due to the announcement of the Oxbridge Throwdown teams. As always, we are grateful that our members are willing to represent the gym... this year we host it. Exciting – and will take a big effort this coming week to make sure everything is ready! Thanks in advance to all the judges, volunteers, athletes and supporters for getting stuck in and making it a good day!

What could have gone better this week...

Systems – still a couple of leaks that need plugging, which should make life easier. Over the last couple of weeks, I've tried to look with a non-emotional eye at certain areas and try to establish the weakness in them. It's allowed me to see a couple of glaring holes that should allow a tightening-up of the services we provide.

Lastly, the story of American Airlines. They came under massive fire for something recently. They took the number of olives in their salad from two to one... it saved them a decent amount of money, but as a result they have had so much negative press that they have probably lost just as much custom as a result. Here's a question: should American Airlines have taken the olive out... or should they have just added the 50 cents to each person's flight to cover the cost? Would you notice 50 cents or 50p extra on the cost of a flight, or would you notice that the salad you got only had one olive? Either way, it's interesting that the extra 50 cents probably could have kept the thousands of satisfied customers.

Enjoy your Easter break!
#buildthechain

MONDAY

April 2: Monday rambles...

Cheating in the sport... So here's something you may or may not know about me... I don't watch the news, in fact, I loathe it. I wait for someone else to filter it for me and tell me about it.

EASTER MONDAY CHEATING IN SPORT

Why? Well, about six years ago I realised I woke up and watched the news, and not one story was about something positive... NOT ONE. So, decided to not watch it. Guess what, no negative thoughts first thing equalled better mood! Yes, I may not know what's going on in the news that everyone loves to know about, but the trade-off I think is a lot less negativity. Plus, if it's really important, someone will tell me about it... and if it's really, really important, I will go and look it up.

Anyway, I heard the story about the cheating in cricket. My immediate response was... name me any sort of team where someone doesn't 'cheat'... Rugby, hands in the ruck, intentionally slowing the ball down... cheating. Football, a tug on the shirt, holding down going for a header... cheating. In any sport, there's the opportunity to take advantage of a situation. As controversial as it is, it's common practice in the sport to try and get away with as much as you can... If they get caught, is that much worse than Neil Back winking the European Cup for Leicester against Munster by taking the ball out of the scrum half's hands at the final scrum? Did he get news stories calling for bans, fines, etc? Nope...

So, the question comes, when is cheating acceptable, when does it cross the line? I remember watching a documentary on Netflix about the 'Little White Lies' – ones that we can justify to ourselves because of X and Y. In sport, if we didn't have the tendency to cheat half the time, we wouldn't even need a referee or umpire.

So, they have received a year-long ban from the game, is that enough or is it too much? In other sports, should we start handing out bans for longer periods? In rugby, for example, should we see longer bans for dangerous tackles? I mean, one sport gives a year ban for trying to alter the outcome of the game, the other gives six weeks for something that could potentially lead to a broken neck...

Monday rambles... a bit serious really aren't they? Maybe a joke to finish...

Q. How does the Easter Bunny stay fit?

A. Eggs-raise and hare-robics!

#buildthechain

TUESDAY

April 3

Today's rambles come as a continuation from last week's KISS principle... today, TRAINING.

WHAT IS THE PURPOSE OF IT?

Simple... in any training, the principle driving factor is IMPROVEMENT, be it cardio, strength, muscle size. Progression drives that.

You can't give the body the same stimulus every session for a year and expect change to occur. If you always do a 5km run at the same pace for a year, you're not going to get fitter... you're going to hit a certain level and stay there. Therefore, progressive programming must occur – that's principle 1.

Principle 2 is that across a period of time, you must use all the musculature of your body. How much depends on the frequency of training and your goal.

Principle 3 is that training should be biased towards the goal that you are seeking. There's no point in doing a 5km run every day if your goal is to have the body of a bodybuilder. Align your training with your goal.

That's pretty much it for KISS:

- Needs to be progressive
- Needs to incorporate all musculature of the body
- Needs to align with your goal.
- Keep It Stupid Simple and

#buildthechain

WEDNESDAY

April 4: Wednesday rambles

Commit to constant and never-ending improvement... truly commit and you can achieve ANY health and fitness journey you embark on!

As a coach, there is one thing above all others that we see that fills us with more pride, more happiness and more satisfaction than anything else. It makes us believe in our mission, it makes us willing to give more, it makes us invigorated and it makes us want to spread even more health to everyone else... when our client, student, member, friend TAKES ACTION.

I've highlighted it before, but the best programme, the perfect nutrition programme or the perfect night's sleep is irrelevant if you don't or can't implement it.

Yesterday, the dads group sat and we chatted nutrition for the hour. Hardly any actual nutrition theory was talked about... nope, they have that knowledge. What was lacking was the PLANNING aspect... how to cook those meals in a way whereby they could just 'do it', rather than have the excuse of not understanding how to do it. One barrier removed. They can now take clearer ACTION, which

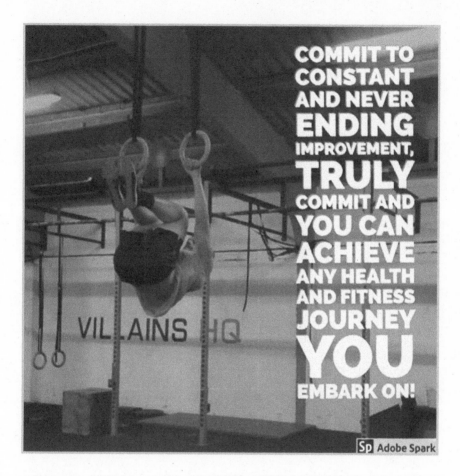

I'm sure now they will. In four weeks' time, when they are all four weeks closer to their goal, pride, satisfaction, belief in the mission and a newly invigorated purpose will floor this coach's brain.

So, this is a plea from a coach to potential clients and other people's clients: if you hire us or if you join us, PLEASE take action. We are here to help you find the way, we are here to HELP you... don't fight it, do your best. There will be ups and downs, but never think that we are doing something other than what we believe is the best way for YOU to hit YOUR goals.

#buildthechain

SATURDAY

April 7

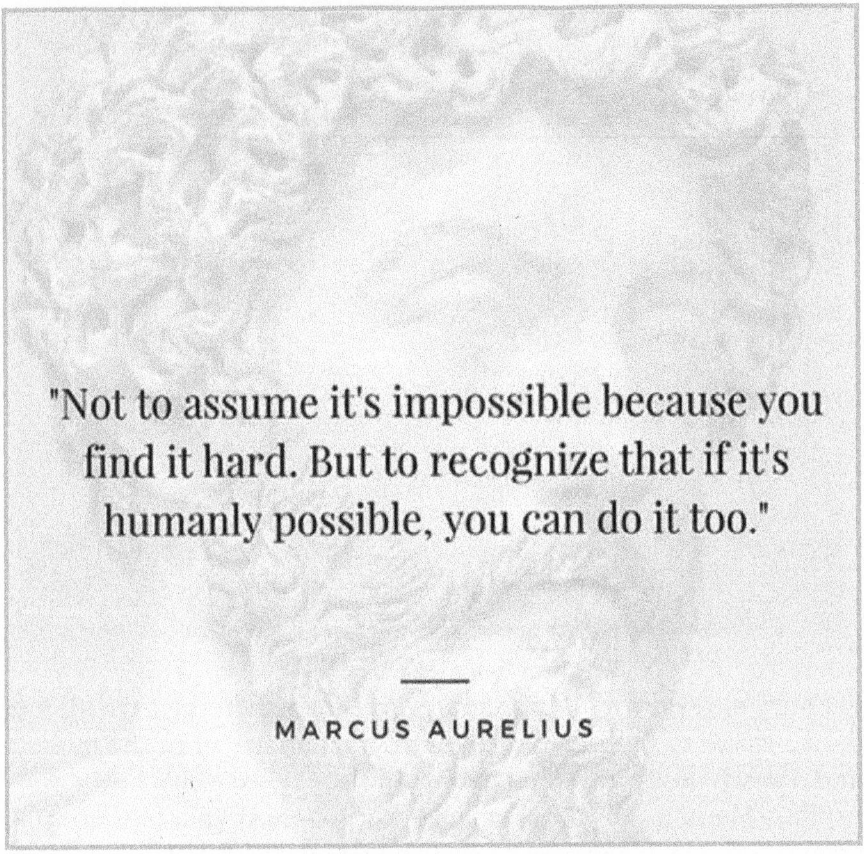

"Not to assume it's impossible because you find it hard. But to recognize that if it's humanly possible, you can do it too."

———

MARCUS AURELIUS

Gameday, there's nothing like it... even more so as a team. The excitement, the nerves, the building of butterflies as the workout or sport gets closer. Please enjoy today — it's the greatest feeling when you're in the thick of it... the adrenaline, the fight or flight. Those in a team today who have done it before look after those who haven't... it can be scary if you think you're alone. Every single one of you can smash today, but remember, it's adult PE!

We've watched our members progress over a short time and a long time, but one thing every member at our gym can be proud of is effort. Give it everything and the result is what it should be... If it helps, in my head I always felt the result was out of my control. The only thing I could control was my effort and desire to win. Regardless of the result, I always had fun and I always won... that's my view of the sport. Might help today...

#toodeepforasaturday #goodluck #youreallwinners #cheese

MONDAY

April 9: Sorry, it's late! Monday rambles...
quick one today!

Who do I listen to? Currently, for me, there's a podcast that I can't get enough of. It is owned and hosted by a former course lecturer who I had the good fortune to be taught by on a few occasions. The name... EcoBolic Radio by Derek Woodske. Derek is a former international level hammer thrower who transitioned into the strength and conditioning world having worked in the NFL among other posts. He now, thankfully for us, spends his time training his clients, I believe in the Middle East, while spreading his message and getting some amazing humans on his podcast. I think most of them have been high level and then also had a shift in mindset and values and transitioned into another calling.

It's intelligent, questioning, full of stories. When he doesn't have a guest, he talks on subjects dear to him. The 'Adult Dose'

episodes from some people would be dull, but Derek's views are engaging and mind-expanding.

Go listen. Today's ramble is about learning. I've given you the key, so open the door and listen.

#buildthechain

TUESDAY

April 10: Going to the archives today for the daily rambles...

Yesterday I even spoke to one of my clients about this – the concept of the 'cost/benefit ratio'.

In life, in training, in health and in every decision you are faced with, you make a conscious or unconscious choice depending on what it costs you vs how much it benefits you. When the benefit outweighs the cost, you 'purchase'.

When you think about it, if you go back through every minor and major decision, you really do weigh up in your mind whether the cost outweighs the benefit, or whether the benefit outweighs the cost.

Let me tell you a story... it's kinda silly but it illustrates the point. When I was at school, maybe aged around 11 or 12, there was a window. This window was above the kitchens of the school, which had a slanted roof. As a 12-year-old, I imagined the distance from the window to the roof to be probably 100ft – to us kids, it was a HUGE drop, but in reality it was probably only 6ft. No one dared jump from the window to the roof – the cost (breaking a leg) outweighed the benefit (glory). Well, a kid with ADHD (in a slightly hyperactive state) only needs the right moment for someone to dare him, and so the challenge was on! I remember thinking in that moment that the glory of the achievement was going to be so much more than anything bad that would happen to me as a result. I jumped... I landed... I screwed up my ankle! Probably because of landing on a sloped roof I twisted it, but nothing major. The benefit... massive reputation gained throughout the school as the boy who jumped!

Granted, it's a silly little story but for some reason, at that moment, the benefit outweighed the cost. That single moment could have ruined my career as a sportsman, and I might not ever have gotten into this field as a result. Go with me here – it's the same when a person has a lapse in their nutrition. That one moment where you think, 'F*#@ it, I'll jump and deal with the consequences later.' So, you overindulge, you splurge. What happens next? Well, if you're lucky, you suffer a 'twisted ankle' (a small consequence). But, if you're like 80% of the population, it ends in a 'broken ankle/leg'... a haemorrhage that leads to a week of underreporting on nutrition, a week off your plan, and a real setback that leaves you feeling guilty, annoyed at yourself, and wondering 'what's the point?'.

So, what we really need to delve into is WHY you might 'jump'. I don't have all the answers, but here are some possible reasons:

1. The benefit is not firmly established. A lot of people pluck goals out of thin air... they get them from the media, or they just randomly come up with a number/size etc. They don't really understand WHY it will be advantageous for them to get to a certain goal.

TIP 1: ESTABLISH THE ACTUAL BENEFIT

- Attract a partner who loves you.
- Gain social status.
- Improve your chances of getting a job (studies have shown that the more obese you are, the less likely you are to get a job at an interview).
- Reduce your risk of dying. A lot of people join the gym or get in touch with me after a health scare.

2. The true cost is not properly understood. Being unhappy SUCKS, but most people do their thinking with their wallet. It's not until you realise that YOU are the limiting factor and not your wallet, that you truly understand the cost which is in your head.

TIP 2: UNDERSTAND THE REAL COST (going off the things above)

- A lifetime of being alone and wishing you could find someone.
- Always being the one in the crowd who people make fun of or at their expense.
- Not realising your full potential and offering it to the world.
- Dead (a fairly useless thing to be).

I see people struggling with their goals all the time – something always gets in the way. It may well do, but that's because *you allow it to*. That cake, that social occasion when you just couldn't resist... when in fact a lot of the time, YOU COULD. In extreme circumstances, think 'GUN TO YOUR HEAD' – would the cost/benefit be different? That's how much your goal should mean to you. When it doesn't, that's when you slip up.

Now, there are chemical and psychological reasons why somebody might slip up... but that's a slightly different matter. However, it's amazing when you actually look at the cost/benefit and break it down, and actually think about it when you make those decisions. If you do, then it becomes apparent that you and only YOU have the power to commit to your goal. Blaming someone else or a situation is just you saying that the benefit did not outweigh the cost. Simple but effective thinking.

As a coach I am here to guide you and to help you be accountable... to be there when you need encouragement and help. In that particular moment, however, only YOU can make it happen!

#priority6 #buildthechain

WEDNESDAY

April 11: Wednesday rambles

From listening to a podcast this morning, the importance of making your training a social event is this ramble's theme. We are not designed to be lone wolves... there may be alpha wolves, but no one needs to walk alone! Train with your tribe!

I can't think of a better example of this than what we have at P6. Those who do the best train with others, others who are better than them in certain areas and ones who they are better than. The collective is stronger than the individual.

I've trained alone, I've trained in groups, I've trained in pairs, in threes... In terms of progress, I've always trained better, pushed harder and gained more when I'm not by myself.

Sometimes you have to... it's better than not training at all, so it's not an excuse. But when you can find strength in the collective... grasp it, keep it close, find people you enjoy spending your time with, laugh, smile, get serious, push each other to be better, call out the weaknesses and work on them.

Find a group of people on the same journey or those who have walked that path.

#buildthechain

THURSDAY

April 12

Thursday rambles... Listening to another podcast today struck a chord... what's my goal for a new member or client?

It's simple really: depending on where they are currently at in terms of health, fitness and wellness, it's to make them better. Move them up a category...

- Thrive
- Well
- Sick

If they are sick, we need medical assistance alongside our programming and monitoring.

If they are well, they are absent of disease, but in my mind, they exist. They have more to offer the world, untapped potential.

If they are thriving, they have several of the aspects of nutrition, sleep, recovery, training and strength in line. This is the ultimate. What they choose to do with it... compete in the sport, look awesome naked, know they have limited their chance of disease, boundless energy, mental clarity and vision... is up to them.

My goal is for our community to thrive, move people up the categories. Wherever they are at, whatever the complications or the hardships, as a community we can handle it. As an individual... it's a lonely world!

Obviously, we listen to the goal of the individual... it's the most important goal. But along the way, you can't avoid the movement along the continuum.

#buildthechain

FRIDAY

April 13: REflection Friday!

Sooo, end of the week... what's gone well, what needs improving, where has your energy been, where could you bring someone in to help?

The first reflection comes from looking back at the staggering performances of everyone at the Oxbridge Throwdown. Whether Rx or Scaled, the comp was hot. The introduction of the swim, the bike, the run took people out of their comfort zones, both physically and mentally (probably emotionally too), but everyone gave everything they had. Smiles on, ups and downs, tension and excitement.

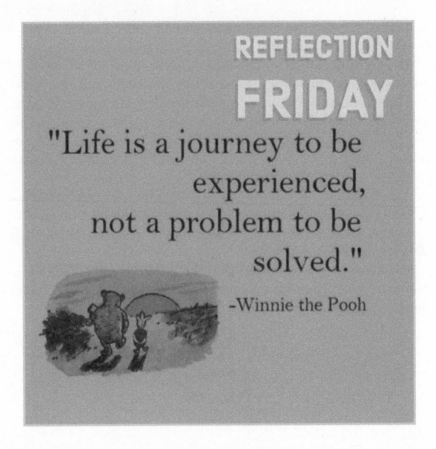

REFLECTION
FRIDAY
"Life is a journey to be
experienced,
not a problem to be
solved."
–Winnie the Pooh

The advancement of the standard was plain to see: personal bests and full-on EFFORT... you can't do better than your best!

Since then, there's been a typical excitement and move-on from the event to the next goals. We've had newcomers to the gym. We've had the build-up in excitement to the starting of the Fit to Care Group... have a search for this group on Facebook – it's a great message. This group training initiative has been set up and funded by sponsored money to try and help carers have a fitness class to teach them to lift and increase their strength and fitness to cope with the demands of caring for a family member or loved one or when working in the field. It's tough trying to lift and move another human, whether they are a newborn or an 18-year-old. This group should help these people look after themselves and stay injury free! A carer with a bad back is of no use to anyone! If you know of any carers in the Abingdon/Oxford area, please pass on the details of the Fit to Care Group. Remember to Build the Chain... the more who know, the more they feel supported!

For myself:

Training... gone well, couple PBs. Some great conditioning work, been able to blow off some steam this week after feeling a bit tired and sore last week. New exercises in the rotation and some singles to see where strength is at. I always forget, especially in the upper body lifts, I'm much better at 1 rep than 2 or 3.

Nutrition... constant as ever. Constant doesn't mean boring, it means educated and knowing what you can and can't have. It means variety within the contexts of what your limits are. The nutrition of clients doing the best: they take the time to understand, they follow what you give them, they hit their protein goal, they fuel their workouts and they reach out when in need.

Business... we've re-launched our original offer of the year of 50% off the first month. It seems to have given us the greatest opportunity to reach the most amount of people. That's the goal... grow the tribe, Build the Chain. The more people we help, the greater the reach and the greater the impact.

So next week...

More efficiency of time is the goal... that's the only goal. Everything else is a constant. Enjoy training and moving.

#buildthechain

MONDAY

April 16: Monday rambles, let's set the scene.

Two lengths walking lunges... length one done, you turn, you start, you're starting to feel it about halfway down. You pass the bench press, which is the next exercise. You probably have six

Things I'm looking forward to tomorrow:

Breakfast
Lunch
Gym
Dinner

ANYONE ELSE?

Sp Adobe Spark

more steps to go... 1...2...3...4...5...then walk to the bench press. What about the sixth?!?!?!

A phrase I love, 'HOW YOU DO ANYTHING IS HOW YOU DO EVERYTHING'.

Cheat yourself out of that one step in lunges and it's likely it won't be the only thing you're going to scrimp on. Over time, 3, 5, 8 years, all those missed reps add up! You'll probably be the person who has a little extra when you're trying to diet down because that one thing won't hurt. You'll probably also think that that last 500 steps of daily activity don't mean that much. You'll probably be the person who sits there at night watching something on Netflix and just watches one more episode because sleep's not that important. You see how you do anything gives me the idea of how you do everything. Over time, 3, 5, 8 years, all those missed reps add up!

Here's the person who gets accelerated progress...

- Completes the reps and asks, 'a) was that good, and b) can I go up in difficulty?'
- Hits their nutrition target and asks how they could have improved.
- Reports back with feedback that they have been trying to hit the sack earlier in order to get more sleep, and asks how they can improve their sleep routine.
- Basically, finds excuses to improve rather than excuses as to why they didn't hit their targets.

One thing I think is fundamental, though, for health, wellness and fitness... do the work. Never scrimp on reps... never finish knowing that you had more reps to do but chose out of laziness to not do them.

Remember, how you do anything is how you do everything!

#buildthechain

THURSDAY

*April 19: Thursday rambles! If it is to BE,
it's up to ME...*

There's a well-known phrase – 'if it's meant to be, it will be' – but really that's only part of the story. You see, we can influence that little phrase. We can do a lot of things to ensure or steer that course by our actions and habits. It's not wholly reliant on the universe to provide... most of it comes down to us, ourselves.

- Commit to your goals.
- Be relentless in your actions towards achieving your goals.
- Take responsibility for your actions and habits and change them in line with what you are trying to achieve.

You have the power to do all of the above...

What if you took your limiting beliefs and put them in a box, locked them away and went all in?

Who would you be then? Where would you be?

I'll tell you where... where you were meant to be... and it will be.

#buildthechain

FRIDAY

April 20: REflection Friday.

REflection Friday. I'm old... that's all... With age, though, comes new exciting times. No responsibility is greater than that of being a parent. It's a magical blend. Ultimately, your kids become whatever you teach them.

Enjoy the sun, #buildthechain

MONDAY

April 23: Monday rambles.

Teamwork... I don't think there's anything in a sport that I love to see more than teamwork. It requires so much of what makes us human for it to occur – some automatic, some taught, some learnt – but when it happens, it's beautiful to see.

On Saturday I went to watch a team CrossFit comp which was slightly different to the normal ones... no rig, no heavy complexes, pure grunt work, speed, the accuracy of movement, endurance. It was run smoothly, people were smiling, no pressures.

We had three teams – one that had worked together before, and two that had trained together on and off because of team WoD (best class of the week).

Regardless of results, the communication between our athletes was plain to see. They talked and strategised. They played to each other's strengths and weaknesses, they encouraged. They timed their reps based off the best outcome for the team, not for the individual. And as a result of what happened... THEY ALL ENJOYED THE EXPERIENCE. It's great that the ladies came second and stood on the podium, but the real thing that came out of it is that each one of the teams would a) compete again and b) compete again TOGETHER, because they worked together, suffered together and came out better athletes.

Teamwork is a beautiful thing. To watch someone whose standard is being raised because of the group, who is being pushed because they want to add to the group, who is being appreciated for their efforts to drive the machine... that's all part of it. That's what the gym should be: a team of individuals all seeking improvement through collective encouragement and working together. Those not part of the team either sink... change gyms regularly... or swim with the rest. It's only a matter of time!

#teamP6 #buildthechain #ourchainisstrong

TUESDAY

April 24: Tuesday rambles...

THE TIMING IS NEVER PERFECT. 'For all of the most important things in life, the timing always sucks... The stars will never align and the traffic lights of life will never all be green at the same time.' – Tim Ferris.

Today is the day... take ACTION, just DO.

I have seen it so many times over the years – procrastination, waiting for things to be perfect before doing something.

Here's what I have seen and heard before: 'I need to get a bit fitter before coming to the gym' or 'I will join but I'll start next month, because this month I've got my birthday and a couple of parties to go to, so I want to join when I can really commit'.

GUESS WHAT, neither of these people ever joined the gym. Why? Because they were waiting for this imaginary perfect moment where the stars align and they are ready to join...

I'll let you into a secret... it doesn't exist. You are wasting time, you are putting it off because the change is uncomfortable and potentially you don't really know what you are doing. It's SCARY. It's EMBARASSING. It's HARD. It's INTIMIDATING... These things are all excuses or barriers that will go through your head, because you know something has to change but you are SCARED!

I can understand everything you are going through. As a gym owner and long-time lover of the fitness space, it seems ridiculous to people when I tell them that I get nervous every time I go to a new gym. But it's TRUE... I do. However, what I know now is that it doesn't really matter. The bigger thing is that I want to IMPROVE, and I love training and searching for new RESULTS.

There is never a PERFECT time to join a gym or hire a personal trainer. There is, however, the RIGHT time. The right time is in fact NOW. If you are thinking about it, TAKE ACTION, call the gym, email the trainer... however way you want to get in touch with us or them, JUST DO IT. By taking that imperfect spur of the moment action, you will have taken a bigger step than you ever have done in the past. You will have invested in YOURSELF, and you flipping deserve it. You can't put a price on your health... the physical, the mental, the emotional. You can't put a price on being able to run around with your kids or to feel confident enough to ask a girl or guy out on a date. These are all the things that can come as a result of the gym, but not any gym though. It has to be one where the environment breeds success, support, knowledge, results, commitment to you, where the trainers care, and where they have private forums for their staff and members to interact and give value, even when they are not within the walls of the gym.

There is never a perfect time to join a gym and to commit to results... but there is TODAY...

I'll even take the hard part out – here's my email address: *enquiries@priority6.co.uk*

#buildthechain

WEDNESDAY

April 25: Wednesday rambles.

So, yesterday's ramble was about taking action regardless of the timing, because ultimately that stars-aligning moment is that of films, fairy tales and love stories. But what happens when you do TAKE ACTION... what next?

Well, there are a few ways to go about the what next. I believe in planning, in having something to refer to... that's across the

board in life. I use whiteboards for things I need to see daily. I use A4 diaries for my day-to-day planning. I have systems by which if I stick to, I know I will head in the right direction.

I learnt these over years of coaching from other people, reading, listening, paying attention to success, finding people who are where I want to be. Success leaves clues, as they say.

What'd be the easiest way to save for something? Here's my way of doing it.

- Say I have a holiday I need to save for that costs £2000 and it's a year away.
- I then break it down into the smallest useable data I can: £2000/12 months = £166/month.
- Then break down into weeks: £166/4 weeks, so around £41/week...

I now know that one session I provide each week needs to go in a pot (or a savings account) for the year. Now I have a plan, I can a) do it or b) forget about it, but at least now I know what I need to do in order to get my goal.

It's the same for fitness, health, weight loss, strength and skill acquisition, apart from the savings account or the pot. Instead, you need a mental storage unit, one that you can't necessarily SEE. It would be like you putting money in the savings account, but not being able to physically see the total or the accumulated wealth. You just have to trust that as you pay the man, it's getting bigger without you ever knowing how much is in there.

So, just like the money you need to set the goal. It's a long-term thing... the resulting goal.

Next, you break that down into chunks of time.

... and now into the actions that need to happen in order for you to hit that target. So instead of the delivering of a PT session, it could be the frequency of gym visits. Then... you continue to take action. You've been through the door before, you know what to expect... now, you just keep turning up. Just like that bank account, the wealth grows, the knowledge grows, the fitness and health grow... But guess what? You don't get £2k overnight... you let it accumulate! There may be a week where you're ill and you can't pay in. That's fine... either you work harder the next week so you can add an extra session and pay £82, or you wait a bit longer.

Over time, the wealth grows... over time, you improve. Unless you win the genetic lottery, it will be an endurance race of you vs you with all sorts of obstacles. Trust in yourself and your ability to get through, over, under, in, out or around them, and just BE in that moment. Accept it, embrace it, things happen. If you know you're on a journey, then it's all part of it.

Here's the cool part: you don't have to do it alone. More on that tomorrow... until then #buildthechain

MONDAY

April 30: Monday rambles...
The dissolution of the minor details.

Nowadays, it's all about the finer details. I get it... I do it in some areas of life that I probably shouldn't. I should probably focus on the bigger items.

Here are the big things you should focus on:

Nutrition
1. Hit your protein requirements. Simply, if you don't, you can't recover and repair broken-down tissue. That means you can't get stronger, that means you can't recover from illness, that means you are sub-optimal.
2. Get enough fats for your hormonal system to produce your hormones.
3. Eat enough carbohydrates to drive your activities. If you are sedentary, you don't require as much as a manual labourer, even if you trained the same amount and had the same muscle mass.

Training
1. Get stronger. That comes in any realm. In the weights room, that's weight on the bar. In yoga, that's the complexity of exercise or the ability to hold a pose longer. Just get stronger in whatever mode you are doing.
2. Make it progressive. Each session search for improvement.
3. Make it appropriate. Until you can squat, deadlift, bench, pull up your own bodyweight... you probably don't need to focus on anything else. See 1.

Supplements
1. If your nutrition isn't at the stage where you are 85% on point... don't bother. There's more you can get from your nutrition than taking a supplement... the base of the pyramid vs the tip of it!
2. Health supps worth taking: fish oil, multivitamin, greens drink blends.
3. Sports supports worth taking, dependent on training phases and modalities: cyclic dextrin, protein in the form of either EAAs or quality protein from a source you can tolerate.

To simplify it even further:

- Eat protein, veg every meal. Eat carbs around your workouts.
- Train hard (relative to you). Whatever you did the last session... beat it.
- Supps. If the above two aren't happening, don't bother. If they are, take 3g of fish oil a day, take a quality multivit and start your day with a greens drink. If you're training over 55 mins, take a blend of cyclic dextrin and EAAs during your workout.

Tried to make that bigger picture as simple as possible. Now get after it, go for it, have a great week, choose happiness daily, do things that make you happy... one shot, one opportunity. Do you take it or let it slip... mic drop.

#buildthechain

WEDNESDAY

May 2

Afraid no long rambles this morning... just this piece of information: 'Know this... you are deserving of more, you are the architect of your future.'

You are the future, it's within you. You are the influencer. You deserve everything you get, good and bad. These are not random things, but a sequence of events you have attracted.

#buildthechain

THURSDAY

May 3

ONLY GOT 30 MINS TO TRAIN
USE AN
EVERY MINUTE ON THE MINUTE
APPROACH

Ramble from the archive. We're close to the holiday season, and a lot of people stress about losing their fitness and conditioning over the holidays... If this is you and you can't bear training, or perhaps want to give yourself some more wiggle room to enjoy your pudding etc, then it's okay to train! It's ok to create a debt so that you can mentally enjoy your break. After all, we don't work all year round to have to start again when we get back from two weeks off!

So, here's the idea...
Short on time?
Use an EMOM!
Total Body Approach
Holidays are a prime example... not much equipment,
but want a quick calorie burner?

- Minute 1: 15 goblet squats
- Minute 2: 15 flat DB presses
- Minute 3: 15 DB deadlifts
- Minute 4: 15 DB bent-over rows
- 300 reps in 20 mins, or 450 in 30

Now you can get back on that sun lounger and enjoy your drink and pudding in the evening!

Want more holiday workout ideas? Drop us a direct message or email *enquiries@priority6.co.uk*

#buildthechain

FRIDAY

May 4

So, a small Friday ramble as it's usually reflection day, but this week been a bit of an anomaly...

We've all heard the term 'fight or flight'... but we don't talk after about the flip side, do you know what that is?

It's 'rest and digest'. As humans, we were designed while not under attack or in the hunt to do these two things. Somewhere along the way, we've lost track of these and they have turned into 'stress and consume'.

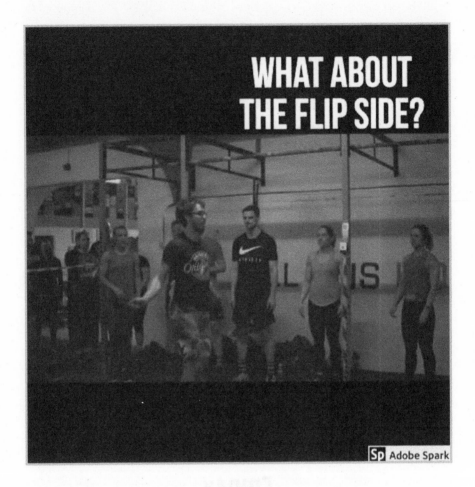

Let's fight for the rest and digest, shall we?

We train hard and we need to rest and recover even harder, to ensure that those minutes spent under the bar or on our feet are translated into new metabolically active tissue and not squandered.

- Sleep
- Eat the right blend of foods

Those two things pretty much cover the large percentage of recovery.

The digest part, I think, refers to two parts. Firstly, the actual sitting, relaxing to eat and concentration on the process of eating.

That means not rushing, that means eating mindfully. The second element is making sure our digestive system can actually digest the foods and is kept healthy through the looking-after of the gut flora. This subject is gigantic and to do it justice on a simple ramble just isn't possible. But consuming a variety of meats, fruit and veg, and a broad range is a great start.

So, people, it's not always about the fight and flight... it's just as much about the need to go into the rest and digest too if you want lasting results!

#buildthechain #imback #hobblingalong

TUESDAY

May 8: Tuesday rambles.

Think like a kid! Kids are so logical, so honest... they take everything so simply.

If you told a child to go burn some energy, what would they do? Well, in our house that would be run around, jump, or do a roly-poly, probably some lunges, press-ups or something on the rings in the garden (we've taught him well). They go for the simplicity option. They don't worry about drop sets, complicated teaming protocols and the finer details... they just... do!

Sometimes when you're starting out, that's the mentality you need... just do SOMETHING, get out and do more than before. Think like a kid. Just turn up, do what you're told to do and have fun doing it!

The sun is shining, so channel that inner child. Our shutter doors are open and waiting for people to come and make lasting changes. The sun elevates everyone's moods... we get outside to

train where we can. Let's go simple this week. Let's just turn up, enjoy and know we are heading in the RIGHT direction, rather than seeking the PERFECT one.

#buildthechain piece by piece

WEDNESDAY

May 9: Wednesday rambles...

Yesterday I posted a piece of text online from Dwayne Johnson (The Rock):

'I don't sell a dream to win championships or gold medals.
I sell a raw concept of life.
We are cracked and scarred.

You're gonna get knocked down and fucked up, but it's in that critical moment when you rise back up, dust yourself off and keep going, that we find success.

No championships. No medals. Just life.

People around the world from different cultures and occupations, getting better daily, putting in the work with their own two hands and earning that dollar.'

#hardestworkerintheroom

This is a guy who has worked hard for everything he has... he's played to his strengths and had massive ups and downs, but he's kept one philosophy throughout his life...

'Be the hardest worker in the room'.

It's a phrase I love. It doesn't mean you have to be the best in the room, the most talented, the fittest, the leanest, the best looking... you know, all the superficial stuff... No, it means be the person with a lion's heart, the person who just continues to give everything, the person who, when the shit hits the fan, works just as hard as before... EFFORT over result. Eventually, EFFORT TURNS INTO RESULT. It just takes time. I'd rather have to work hard at something and sacrifice energy than being given it easily. At the time, it doesn't feel that way but, in the end, when you look back and can see the start point to the end point, it's so much more satisfying to know you had to work hard to achieve it.

Whatever the day, whatever the task, whatever the goal...
BE THE HARDEST WORKER IN THE ROOM!

#buildthechain
#alwaysimprovealwaysevolvenevergiveup

THURSDAY

May 10: Thursday, into the archives...

In ALL examinations or assessments in life, they only show you what happened at that moment in time. They don't tell you that you have lost 20kg before that week where you didn't lose anything, if you're being assessed weekly. They don't tell you that you have increased your chin-ups from 1 to 10 over a period of five weeks, if you just think of that one assessment that you had four weeks in.

More importantly, they don't tell you how far you can go! They don't show you your potential. Take some of the greatest minds for example. Gary Vaynerchuk got Ds and Fs in school… if he had let that define him, he would be nothing. Today, he runs a multimillion-dollar company and is considered a hustling genius by many. Richard Branson was terrible at school… if he had let his exams define him, he may never have become the entrepreneur he is today.

It's the same in sport or fitness or in relationships. There are tests along the way that will show some form of progress, but don't let that define how far you can go. Dream big, dare to fail and you too can exceed even your own expectations.

#buildthechain #bepositive #believeinyourprogress

FRIDAY

May 11: REflection Friday.

A week of progress in a few aspects of life. That's all we are after on this journey… progress towards an outcome, an outcome that we choose and set ourselves up for by following the most efficient and long-lasting path.

I've listened to a couple of interesting podcasts. I always try to listen to things that challenge what I have done or potentially are not what I currently believe… I say currently because I have the ability to change my beliefs and systems if a better, more effective, methodology arises.

Right, training…

Bit of an odd week, #kneehab going very well, step-ups have been enabled. Otherwise, it's tick over time, with no real training system, rep scheme or goal.

In place, other than the recovery from surgery, it's been difficult to plan out training. Metcons have been modified and have identified sprint recovery as a major area of weakness, so shorter, more intense, bouts will come in the future. The message: there's always something you can do!

Business...

We sat down on Wednesday and put a few more bits together for our new gym guides. We think it's going to become the bible for all new and old members. Very excited to see it unfold.

Some excellent performances from clients this week... personal bests and plateaus broken! The message: effort is rewarded!

Oscar turned five. Two birthday parties in two days left a knackered set of parents, but the sun was shining and it was lovely to see all the excitement unfold.

Next week... the goal, progress, build that chain of events and effort. Great things will happen!

#buildthechain

SUNDAY!

May 13

Transformation Sunday at the gym... it's a thing... back to when we took on double the risk, increased our outgoings by two, and took the plunge, because we believed that what we are doing with our gym mattered and that more people could benefit from it. We could have stayed safe with one unit... it was scary, it was a big commitment, it was the right one!

We love what we do. There are ups and downs, but we smile our way through them, open the door the next day and choose to help others commit to lifelong changes. We've seen more people transform their lives than we thought possible... night and day differences, much like the transformation of our gym. As we grow, as we develop, as we continue – thank you all for being a part of it. I mean that... without each of the people who have walked through those doors, we wouldn't have had all the experiences we have had. We wouldn't have learnt lessons and we wouldn't be anywhere near where we are now. So, on soppy Sunday... thank you! To each of you who have helped us, thank you! Be grateful for the opportunity of change, and be grateful it's within our capabilities and destiny to decide our own paths.

#buildthechain

MONDAY

May 14: Monday rambles.

Here's a phrase all people should live by: 'Always say what you CAN do, not what you can't'.

It's a little bit along the lines of, whatever you say you are or aren't, it's true.

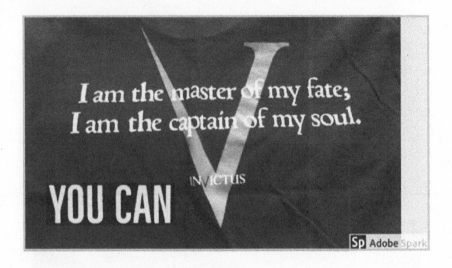

In the CrossFit world, I think Invictus CrossFit got the best phrase up on their wall before anyone else:

'I am the master of my fate;
I am the captain of my soul'.

You can do anything you want to in your fitness and health if you view it as a progressive model. Each day, you can do something towards it, even if you have convinced yourself you can't. It can be so minute that you think it doesn't matter, but it does. It could be that not doing something IS the step towards doing something.

Example
You've had a long day and you are tired... you CAN do a home workout. Is it as good as going to the gym that day? YES! Huh?... but Ollie, don't you want people to come to the gym? Yes, of course I do, but what if they can't make it, or are at their wits end and are about to scream into a pillow and break down in tears at the thought of having to get changed, get to the gym, shower, change, drive back, collect the kids, cook supper, get prepped for a meeting, etc? I'd prefer it if they got a great 30-min workout at home done, stayed less stressed and enjoyed just moving, over the alternative.

So, in this case, you CAN workout, you can still work on your fitness, you can still progress and take a step towards your goals.

Nutrition... everyone can eat healthily. You can choose to base your food around a protein source, with plenty of veggies and carbohydrates, depending on your activity levels. Everyone can make one healthy change a week to their nutrition. Everyone can reach out for help in this area.

Everyone can walk 10 mins a day, or find some way of doing an extra 10 mins of moving to pump blood around their bodies. Could start with just 2 mins every day, and the hormonal cascade of that is very beneficial.

The point is, look at your life today and decide what you can do. The first step for me is to wake up and choose to make today a happy day. I always have a better day when I choose to operate from a happier place.

Monday rambles done. Everyone reading, have a great day... everyone not reading, still have a great day. What can you do today to make it better than the last? For you are the master of your fate and the captain of your soul.

#buildthechain #choosetobemore

TUESDAY

May 15: Tuesday rambles from the archives, but edited.

Simplicity is where to start! All the simplest things in life take you the furthest. The more you can break it down into simple layman advice, the easier the steps are to follow, the greater the adherence and therefore the greater the result!

This is certainly true of fitness, health, training and nutrition.

If a nutrition plan is SIMPLE to follow, guess what? You get more results from it. It causes less time thinking about it, which means less stress, which means less hassle... and we all hate hassle! If it confuses you, tell your coach and they should be able to make it more simplified for you. As time goes on, the plan remains simple as your knowledge base increases. What's simple to one person might be complicated to another... the understanding is what dictates the complexity.

You will get the most results from following a simple to follow programme (don't confuse this with an EASY programme). In essence, hit all the muscles of the body with an overload of some description. This could be more weight, a new exercise, more reps or sets, a longer time under tension, shorter rest periods. Done regularly, the results will come... FACT!

Relationships are simple too – give as much as you can, and you will receive back what you put into it. At P6 we give as much as we can... we have a relationship with each of our members. We give as much as our time and knowledge allow us to. Hopefully, its why our members stick with us for such a long time. Simply... we care!

Enjoy your day, do something simple and reap the rewards from simplicity, rather than conforming to this weird world we live in where complex apparently is better!

Remember, #buildthechain... that means build your knowledge and build your results, link by link!

WEDNESDAY

May 16: Wednesday rambles – a look inside.

Why is my motto

    Always Improve
    Always Evolve
    Never Give Up

I once almost got it tattooed around my upper leg in Afrikaans:

    Altyd Verbeter
    Altyd Ontwikkel
    Nooit Afstaan

Why is it my favourite and go-to phrase?

It hits me on three fronts. I can't concentrate on one thing, so that's kind of appropriate!

Always Improve...

I'm a constant improvement seeker. Take my training diary, for example... I look at the previous numbers and try to beat them. Take my finances... I look at the numbers and try to improve them. My happiness is driven by a constant need to improve. I'm at my best when I have something to improve on, and I can see where I was and where I need to be. It's all self-improvement, though. I couldn't care less if I have improved more or less than someone else... it's about me. Progress excites me, progress drives me.

Always Evolve...

For me, this is about learning and education. I was lucky growing up to go to an amazing set of schools. It wasn't, however, until after school that I realised the importance of education and self-learning. The more you learn, the more you realise that you don't know much. That, in turn, for me is exciting, as there is always more. A never-ending amount of evolving and improvement. That's not a negative thing... it's a thirst for knowledge about subjects that are exciting and lead to opportunities. It's about having subjects to get excited by, and the knowledge that a new subject will arise out of them.

Never Give Up...

I struggled with this one for years, as it has a 'negative' ending... 'give up'. It is the last thing you hear, which isn't a very positive statement... that is, until I realised that negatives drive me as much as positives. Negatives push me away... I can't handle negativity, so it drives me away from it. Now, the Never Give Up statement drives me to do exactly that. In a shit spot, you won't see me give up – I'll work out a way, I'll find a path.

There you have it. If I could sum up my thought process and life in general, this motto is it. Simple, effective and just a few words but with a huge amount of thinking and belief behind it.

#buildthechain was born from this thought process... constantly adding to the links, improving and evolving. If the chain gets broken, never give up – just build it again link by link, to evolve into a new longer chain.

Have a great day and 'Always Improve, Always Evolve, Never Give Up'!

THURSDAY

May 17: Thursday rambles...

A different way of thinking about your goals! Now, most people will teach that there are many steps in order to get to your goal, or what you want to achieve. That is correct... there are many steps. These could be a change in nutrition, a change in your training habits, a simple change in activity levels, or even seemingly minute changes in drinking more water!

However, I was listening to a podcast the other day and the following sentence rang powerfully in my mind:

'Our entire life can change in an instant when you decide you are worth more.'

You see, it doesn't take 10 steps, five top tips, etc – it actually takes a flip of a switching moment when YOU decide to change. That one moment when you say to yourself, I am worth more! The 10 steps come after that, as do the five top tips to drop body fat or the 30-day challenge. They all come after that MOMENT of clarity when, for some reason, you believe you NEED to change... not WANT to change, but NEED to change.

Something may have happened to you – a health scare, a glance in the mirror, a comment, a feeling... But, at the end of the day, it's that instant moment where YOU decide YOU are worth more!

You can have many of these moments in your life, each one leading to something GREAT, something POSITIVE... a change in YOU and an UPGRADE of your life...

You don't need to look for these moments, they will just happen. Once they do, EMBRACE them, take imperfect ACTION, seek out help, seek out the person most suited to helping you... the person armed with the expertise to guide you and teach you. Don't let them pass you by – it will only lead to regret and pain. Become the person you want to be!

#buildthechain

FRIDAY

May 18: REflection Friday.

Do you ever have those days of just extreme happiness? Well, yesterday was one of those days. Now, before I get ahead of myself, it was a FEELING of happiness, a moment, a realisation that things can be undone today, but yesterday in isolation was a great day. We all have days that are a bit gloomy, where we feel pissed off and nothing goes right. Quite often we dwell on those days. Well, instead of that, I'm concentrating on yesterday, a day where I got to come in and open the doors to our gym (10 years ago that was a pipe dream, a distant wish. Not only that, but there were people stood outside ready to go, ready to improve, wanting to train... they don't HAVE to be there, they WANT to be there). I then got to guide multiple people through the process of making their lives better via the mode that I know how – physical and mental training. I believe entirely that the key to happiness is a body that is healthy. Call me biased or naive, but I genuinely believe that your life improves with physical exercise as the driving force.

Then I got to go home and eat amazing food, with the sun shining and my baby girl giggling and laughing, and wifey laughing at our landlord asking to touch my topknot. I then got to take our doggy out for a relaxing sunny walk while interacting with his nuts mentality and listening to Lils blowing raspberries in my ear. She then fell asleep, so got to interact with clients and friends via Messenger... something I don't get enough time to do usually. Collected Oscar from school. They are preparing for the Royal Wedding Party, so he had glitter in his hair, a smile on his face and then asked to eat basically the contents of the house... he's growing again! Sun still shining, sat outside on our front step watching Oscar and Chase play, listening to summer songs and making silly faces at Lils. I mean, when you reflect, you just realise that the day has been pretty awesome.

Not all days are like that, but when they are, APPRECIATE THEM, dwell on them. As I walk around this morning, the sun shining again, I'm thinking, how can I make today even better? Maybe it's reaching out to a new prospective member, knowing that their life will never be the same. Maybe it's to write down a new idea which pops into my head that is the next challenge or chapter. Who knows? What I do know is that yesterday was great, but today could be better if I want it to be... if I let it be...

This week has had its ups and downs. The knee... definitely on the mend. Arms... definitely bigger than my calves.

Business is thriving and moving towards the product we want it to be.

The weekend ahead should be fun, and, of course, we have regionals CrossFit to keep us interested as well. On that, good luck to all our British athletes, but good luck and well done to everyone there. It's a huge achievement... dedication and hard work got you there. You already so freaking enjoy it... what will be will be.

That's it, enjoy your Friday... I will.
#buildthechain

MONDAY

May 21

Create a team of people around you who can help you move towards your goal. If they aren't there to better you, get rid of them to stop them from influencing your goal.

Don't choose training partners who are late and who cancel on you all the time. Choose dependable ones, ones who lift you up. Ones who are there to work as hard on themselves as you want to work on yourself. Chat before, then do the work, then chat after. The time for work is the time for WORK.

CHOOSE TO SURROUND YOURSELF WITH A TEAM OF PEOPLE WHO WANT YOU TO SUCCEED

 Adobe Spark

If your partner doesn't help your nutrition, don't get rid of them, ha-ha... have the conversation with them. Communicate your desires and why quite often they simply aren't aware of why you want to improve.

Basically, surround yourself with people who bring you UP, those who want success for you, whether you have to pay for it or not. If you choose people who doubt you, you will doubt yourself.

Quick one this am, as had a consult with two people who are going to train together... teamwork makes the dream work.

#buildthechain

TUESDAY

May 22: Tuesday we go to the archive...

There was a great advert around the Olympics of Michael Phelps. It portrays the fight of an Olympic champion... the hours of hard work and dedication in the 'darkness' that brings about this champion when he steps into the arena or the 'light'.

It's an incredibly motivating and powerful video from Under Armour UK, which probably hit home with a lot of people.

Bring that down to us non-Olympians and the same philosophy rings true. Consistency and work in the gym and in the kitchen along with our recovery methods ensure that when we step into the light, we are a better, more powerful, version of ourselves.

Over the years of training people, I have come to discover that what people really want is more than a good body... that's the stepping into the light part. They want to feel like they have control of more aspects of their life, they want to eat healthy foods, they want to train and exercise, they want to sleep better, they want a better sex life, they want to feel happy and loved... But, at the moment, they don't know HOW! Well, they think they do. For a time, a diet or an exercise plan works well, but as time goes on, the WORK IN THE DARKNESS wanes, not because they don't want to work, but usually because there is a lack of accountability or they get bored. We all work better with a coach, which is why I have a coach for training, a coach for nutrition and a business coach. Why? Because I have someone to report to, someone who will tell me if I'm doing enough work in the darkness, when no one is watching, when it's all on me. I have always worked better with a coach. I think that's also why CrossFit works so well... the coach leads you, they motivate you. By having to book onto a class, there is a sense of accountability... you have other friends in the class who notice if you are not there, they call you and ask why, or say that they 'missed you today'. Want to go a bit further and delve deeper into what you have to offer? Personal training or remote programming... they have been set up to increase your accountability, to have that commitment to doing the work in the 'darkness', so that when you leave the gym, you step into the light and you feel powerful, healthy, energetic and full of self-worth!

So, guys and girls, what can you do in the darkness that ensures that when you step into the light you can feel these amazingly empowering things?

- Commit to hitting enough protein and vegetables in your nutrition.
- Commit to coming to train however many times a week you can (our lives are busy, but one is better than none and 30 mins at home is better than none... ask about the deck of cards workout!)
- Commit to getting to sleep on time.
- Remove junk food from your nutrition at least 95% of the time.
- Commit to becoming a healthier, fitter, stronger, more energetic YOU.

That's it, guys and girls. Whatever you choose to do in the darkness will show in the light. Only you can see what you do in the darkness... do the work and reap the rewards.

OC
Want more information? Follow my Instagram
priority6theocmethod.
#buildthechain #builtthechain

WEDNESDAY

May 23: Wednesday rambles.

Wednesday rambles... here's a concept I like:
    'Don't get mad in traffic'

This actually stands for much more than the simple statement.

Imagine you set off on an hour-long journey, when about 20 mins in... hazard lights are on... traffic jam.

Two options:

1. Get really mad at being held up. Get bothered by it... allow it to ruin your day.
2. Accept it. Carry on listening to the podcast. Use the opportunity to ring a friend. Come out the other side having been productive... use the opportunity wisely.

Really, though, the phrase stands for not letting things outside of your control ruin your journey in life. In life, there are loads of traffic jams, things that will delay you, things that you simply cannot alter. All outside of your control. The only thing you can control is your reaction to them and the habits which you live your life by.

So next time you are stuck in traffic, ring a loved one, learn something on a podcast, listen to a book... anything whereby you come out of that situation a better human!

#buildthechain

FRIDAY

May 25: REflection Friday.

Well, what a week. On a personal level, all sorts of ups and downs... oh the joys of essentially being 'self-employed'.

Anyway, what this week has been a positive for you? How have you built your chain?

"The chief task in life is simply this: to identify and separate matters so that I can say clearly to myself which are externals not under my control, and which have to do with the choices I actually control.

Where then do I look for good and evil? Not to uncontrollable externals, but within myself to the choices that are my own..."

———

EPICTETUS

dailystoic.com

For me, on the training and rehab fronts, it's been exceptionally positive. The knee's on the mend, and my confidence in its integrity is building. It's fine... more work in the last four days than in six months! With a week of loading my body coming up, it's important not to get carried away and do anything silly!

Business this week has been focused on the joy of the GPR (rubbish). That out the way, we will be announcing some big offers as we try to broaden our reach in the local area. For this offer, we are looking to involve the people we already serve, so please watch out!

Short REflection today as I wander up and down the Astro at the gym, typing away like a loser. But I'm here Building the Chain, getting the word out, trying where possible to spread positivity. Yesterday I posted about not worrying about things out of your control. Lo and behold, a post comes up in my feed from Daily Stoic, in which Epictetus said it a lot better than I did! 'Where do you look for good and bad? Not to uncontrollable externals, but within yourself to the choices that are your own...' Those people were far more intelligent than I!

Oh, and don't forget, #buildthechain

MONDAY

May 28

A simple phrase for this morning's rambles, similar to a phrase growing up that weirdly was used in a WWF (WWE nowadays) speech by one of the wrestlers being interviewed... he said, 'when it's all said and done'.

You see, we are here for a finite amount of time... we don't know how much. I want to go through life knowing that I'm planning for the long term (by looking after my body and mind through good nutrition and daily activity), but also enjoying the day I've been given. I don't understand the phrase 'live every day as if it were your last', as otherwise, I'd be reckless. I do understand it in terms of telling those you love that you love them, treating people as to how you want to be remembered and smile.

Back to fitness, I truly believe, for me, that I give the best of myself when I'm eating the right amount for my activity, when I have expended energy on physical activity, and when I have a structure to my life that allows my mind to have freedom of creativity. It doesn't always happen... sometimes you get stuck, but that's when you reach out to your trusted few who help you through and pick you up.

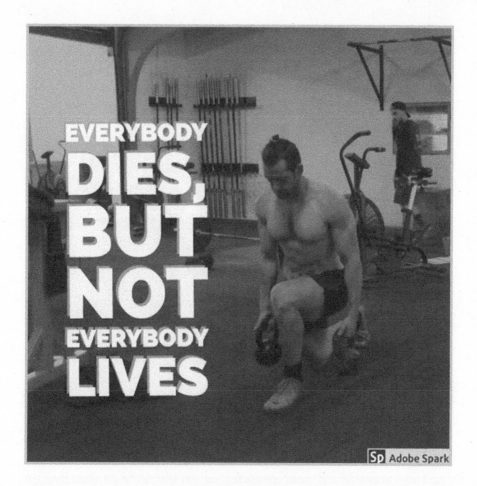

So, one day you are gone. But did you live your life to the full? Did you give the best version of yourself to the world? If not, maybe you could start now, because I'm sure everyone around you wants to see THAT version of you.

#buildthechain

TUESDAY

May 29

Don't hope for a life of no problems, but of good problems to have...

For every problem we have, there is a solution, but with it a new set of problems are uncovered.

Take wealth... a poor person has problems because they are poor, but a wealthier person has problems too – they are just different ones. Every person, no matter their wealth, perceives the problems the same way.

A fit person has problems, as they often hit a point of diminishing returns, where improvements come so slowly that they feel down about it. A new person to fitness has problems, because they feel anxiety just walking through the door, or because every session feels so difficult. In each case, the problem is neither bigger or smaller than the other. The problem for both is valid.

The joy comes in problem-solving, working out the solution to a problem so that the joy can rain down on us... that is until we encounter another problem that was born from that problem.

Take injuries... the problem... find the solution. It may just make you a better athlete or teach you a valid lesson. It certainly does for me each time I learn about a new movement, exercise, stretch, recovery method and it goes into the arsenal.

Embrace problems and find a solution. Don't try to avoid the problems... life would be boring without them!

#buildthechain

THURSDAY

May 31: Thursday rambles.

I saw a poster the other day, which stopped me dead in my tracks: 'STOP SCROLLING FOR A SECOND. PAUSE AND LIST 3 THINGS YOU ARE GRATEFUL FOR.'

We are a scrolling culture now... a quick 2 mins (or 20 mins) scrolling down our feeds, wasting a bit of time on transport, at work, at home. But this actually made me stop.

Instantly, my thoughts were...

1. My family... I was sat with Oscar at the time.
2. The business that myself, Em and Si have developed from a seedling idea, a philosophy that has evolved into what it is today.
3. The genetics I was given... the body and mind. There have been times I have hated it, not strong enough, not lean enough, not clever enough, not talented enough, I wish I could do this and that... But you know what, when I look back, I've accomplished more than I believed I was capable of. I've done it through hard work. I've done it through taking the opportunity when it presented itself, a lot of the time when I have been nervous too or not confident in my ability. I am far from where I want to be. I know I have more to give and a system through which to get there which

STOP SCROLLING FOR A SECOND PAUSE AND LIST 3 THINGS YOU ARE GRATEFUL FOR

constantly evolves. I may not be the outlier or the winner of the genetic lottery, but I'll always work hard, and as long as I'm the inspiration to my children and to those who want to listen and improve their lives through fitness and nutrition... then that's perfect to me.

We all have days and periods in our lives when we need a boost... we all have moments that make us think.
What three things are you grateful for?

#buildthechain

FRIDAY

June 1: Reflection Friday.

Reflection Friday... imagine a country scene. Such a picture paints a thousand words, but here's just a few...

Grateful
Peaceful
Beautiful

The early bird catches the worm
Recovery
Rest
Happiness
Calm
Cirrus clouds are beautiful
Green
Countryside

#buildthechain

THURSDAY

June 7: Thursday rambles!

Just back from holiday and straight back into the morning routine... feels great.

Personally, I think the morning routine has been one of the most powerful and productive additions to my life. It sets me up for the day, highlights the most important things I need to do early and puts them in the forefront of my mind. I learn, I improve and move.

- I get up at the same time every day.
- I listen to a podcast on the way to work.
- I then walk and type a 'rambles' usually on a subject that interests me, I've listened to or I've been thinking about.
- I write my to-do list of the three most important things I need to do today.
- I get back to the gym, ready to go.

Simple effective and healthy for the body and mind.

If you want help developing a routine better suited to health and fitness, just reach out!

#buildthechain

FRIDAY

June 8: REflection Friday.

REflection is a vital part of growth. Sitting down and looking at the last seven days gives you an overview of what went well and what needs work on.

I like to cover three categories:

1. Training and nutrition
2. Business
3. Home

I try to look for three good things and three to work on in each case, and then build out a plan from there. It's not the most complex or advanced method, but it's a routine, and... as we all know... a growth routine brings about productivity and advancement.

So, have a little sit-down and write those categories that mean something to you out. Write three good things and three to work on. Then develop a plan to work on those weaknesses.

#buildthechain

MONDAY

June 11: Monday rambles!!!

The case for a pre-mortem.

   What on earth is that Ollie?

   ... it's the concept of taking your goals, listing them out and then also writing down everything that could stop you from achieving them.

   What use is this?

   ... fail to plan, plan to fail! There is one thing that is certain in fitness goals, health goals, business goals and relationships – it's never going to be plain sailing, and it's not always going to be via the best possible route. There are always going to be issues or problems to solve, and so why not PLAN for them? This way, when they come up, you are prepared, you have seen them and know what to do in that situation. You are prepared!

   Let's take weight loss, seeing as most people have tried to, or are currently trying, to lose weight in the UK.

   You're aiming for 0.5kg a week weight loss. The first three weeks are going well, nailing that loss every time. The fourth-week hit, and nothing moves on the scales... what do we do?

   (A lot of people here would get frustrated, angry even... an I've done all I can scenario. That may well be true, but the body doesn't work in a linear pattern, and there are so many reasons why a scale weight on one day could be an inaccurate representation of your results, but that's a different post.)

   We plan for it... what do we do in that situation?

- We identify any feelings and while recognising them, we also realise that they make us act impulsively.
- We get in touch with our coach (if we have one).
- We make sure that that day, we are spot on with our nutrition.
- We look at our WHY goals, the reasons why you are on this journey, and potentially even write them out again... or say them out loud. Whichever resonates with you.

What we don't do:

- We do not believe we are worthless and have failed.
- We do not go out and binge eat because it was all a waste of time.

- We do not skip our next meal or workout... we are not that sort of person.
- We do not go off plan and try to lose extra weight over the next two days, leaving us feeling tired, fed up, craving and moody.

There are so many situations whereby you can plan the 'what if this, then that'. Depending on your mindset and personality, it can be really very powerful to have a pre-mortem plan. In short, it's been used by some of the most successful out there: the All Blacks, England when they were in their prime in 2002–2003, Michael Phelps, numerous fighters...

So, the task: write out your goals, pre-mortem them, every scenario you can think of. Then, when one comes up... WHICH IT WILL... you will have prepared, you will have confidence, you will defeat your own demons.

Remember, Building the Chain is a day-by-day, win-by-win approach. This will help you build your chain longer and without gaps!

#buildthechain

TUESDAY

June 12: Tuesday rambles.

Keeping it simple and short with the 'cleanse or clog' method... In life, things either help us towards our goals or take us further away from them. So, from today, ask yourself this simple question while looking at a situation, a meal, a decision, a relationship...

Does this cleanse or clog?

You will know which, instantly.

This question gives you back the power of decision making… it will make you stop and consider. Most people have the information, but they just don't know how to apply it or they forget it in times of need. If you ask yourself this question, it will bring awareness to the situation and keep you present. If you are present and not on autopilot, I trust YOU will make the right decision!

#buildthechain

WEDNESDAY

June 13: Rambles from the archives today!
As always, still appropriate!

ARE YOU CRIPPLED BY FEAR??
We all are at some point in life crippled by fear. Can you learn to embrace it? Can you learn to love it? Can you learn to conquer it?

YES...

... BUT IT'S F'ING HARD!

And anyone who tells you differently is a moron, or they don't know what they are talking about.

Let me give you two personal examples.

1. The changing room. As a young rugby player, although I let my playing do the talking on the pitch, every match day brought with it a fear, a huge fear, of taking off my top and feeling judged. It may sound stupid to some, it may seem ridiculous to others. But leading into a match, that feeling was something I feared much more than anything else on

that day. In fact, it's probably one of the reasons I got into fitness in the first place.

How did I overcome this fear? Probably never really did before I stopped playing. But how did I TRY and overcome it? I worked on myself mentally and physically. I trained more effectively. I sought out help from those with more knowledge and those who I respected. I started to READ about self-improvement and changing one's mindset. Essentially, I trained my brain and my body to be a better version. Did it work eventually? Yes!

2. The second situation is completely different and happens around every four weeks of training, usually in the last week of a training phase where the weight has been building and increasing or the reps have increased. Sometimes there is a genuine fear of stepping under that bar... what if I can't do it? But to turn it on its head, I also know that that situation, that right there, is where growth and accomplishment come from! What would be the point of stepping under that bar knowing that I could 100% do what I'm about to do?! You see, that fear of the test is what we need to embrace, not all the time, but some of the time, in order to move forwards. With the right coach as well... they will instil belief in you and they will know whether or not you are capable, because otherwise they wouldn't be fighting your corner for you. Quite often as a coach, I would say I have an unwavering belief in what my clients can achieve – far beyond their own belief... Why? BECAUSE I HAVE WALKED THAT PATH MYSELF!

That second one, particularly, is a hugely valuable lesson for life. You need to get comfortable with being uncomfortable, once in a while. BUT, and that's a big but, CELEBRATE the success when you do! I am a numero-uno classic case of not celebrating, always wanting more and moving on to the next thing without regarding the success of what has just been achieved. That personality type gets me into hot water, as I'm virtually never satisfied. In fact, that's what I will be working on from a personal standpoint this year.

Fear can DRIVE or CRIPPLE us. I have had coaching in the art of overcoming fear. I have put myself in situations of fear, but also surrounded myself with a team of people all striving for success and self-improvement. I have had the fortunate opportunity to sit in a room last September with some truly inspiring people. I have learnt an awful lot, but there is more to come... more to come when I embrace yet more fear and come out on top again!

How do you deal with your fear? Sometimes all it takes is for someone to reach out and tell you that you are not alone (#cheesybuttrue). Perhaps today is that day.

#buildthechain

FRIDAY

June 15: REflection Friday but with a difference!

Why it's so hard to give praise.
When you don't like receiving praise, like myself, or at least find it uncomfortable, you forget sometimes that others do like hearing praise. I don't mind a 'great job, well done', but any more than that and it makes me uncomfortable. It makes me think... I'm just doing my job, I'm just putting the effort in – the result, meh, it's just the outcome of the effort.

While others prefer to lavish praise for each step, I forget that all the time... it's a flaw in my coaching and in my personality. I admire everyone who puts their best step forwards. I was having a conversation with a friend who made me realise this. I keep forgetting to tell people how well they are doing. I keep forgetting to make sure they know I'm proud of them, because I ASSUME that they know that just from my 'good job'. I forget they are not ME!

So, in the interest of building my own chain and hopefully encouraging others to build theirs, I'm going to try to remember at each opportunity to give praise to those who deserve it, no matter how insignificant they may think the step.

#buildthechain

MONDAY

June 18: Happiness is a choice, not a destination.

I love this phrase, as for me it holds true. I choose to be happy, I choose to do the things that make me happy. It's not a destination I will get to once I have this or that, although I used to buy into that mindset. I'm happy all the time knowing that, ultimately, I have the decision on how I view situations and how I react to them. It's not plain sailing – there are of course days when things don't go to plan, when life is unfair, when happiness seems impossible... but it isn't. There is always a silver lining. There is always a happy memory to hold onto.

For me, happiness is in the process, it's in the day-to-day, the chain if you will. I'm thankful for all I have and all I will have in my life, but I'm really thankful for the way to have developed to think. It's been learnt... I definitely wasn't born with the same way of thinking I have now. Over time, it's developed, thanks to the people I've met, the people I have listened to, the friends and the clients who I've been exposed to. I've in essence studied it, probably with more interest than any subject in my schooling time. Mindset and fitness together unlock some pretty spectacular doors.

There are situations that are a bit borderline, but I think you will see the principle. Choose happiness... if someone has passed away, remember the amazing times you have had with them, the happy moments however small. A deal didn't go your way... take from it the lessons you have learnt. Perhaps you could have pitched it in a different way... you have learnt something and you have become better because of it. There are some situations that I'm sure seem impossible to be positive about or take anything from, but somewhere in there, because of adversity, you will become a better person because of it if you are open to happiness. Instead of looking purely at the negative, look for the happiness too. Over time, it may just make you smile!

Every day, wake up and believe you can be happy, move, eat well, treat yourself with respect, hold yourself to your good values, and happiness will be a constant towards your destination.

#buildthechain

TUESDAY

June 19: Tuesday rambles.

We are the sum of what we repeatedly do. Your habits dictate how you live your life and how you are perceived by the

people around you. However, there are certain categories you can break your habits down into when it comes to fitness and health, body composition and performance. For each of the five categories, there are habits that will ensure success and habits that will keep you from happiness and from progressing at the rate you want.

- Training
- Nutrition
- Sleep
- Recovery
- Mindset

An exercise: for each of the five categories above, write down two habits that will lead to success. Keep those in your diary and visit them regularly.

For example:

Sleep:
1. Lights out at 10pm.
2. Wake up at the same time every day and don't hit snooze.

If I was to do those two things and ingrain them as habits, my sleep will improve. I'll get closer to my goals, as sleep is fundamentally essential to human health. Simples.

'Forget the things you can't control, control what you can control'.

Control over concern... most of the things we are concerned about we literally have zero control over. You can't make someone like you, you can't... but what you can do is control your habits and therefore what you stand for. If they then choose to like you or not, you are the person you want to be, so it doesn't matter anyway and it's their issue anyway! Be the person YOU want to be, uphold the habits that are central to your beliefs and values, and the world will look a very different place!

#buildthechain

WEDNESDAY

June 20: Wednesday rambles...Sleep!

Any parent knows it's the pinnacle of success when your child sleeps through the night. For those who don't have children, hold onto that sleep dearly!

A form of torture is sleep deprivation, but not only that, the quality of your sleep is vastly important too! So, what are the sorts of things we can do to maximise our sleep?

For me, the first most important one is having a bedtime and a wake-up time that is set, no matter the day, Monday through Sunday. Think about this logically... say, Monday to Friday you go to bed around 10/11 and wake up at 6/7. Then, Saturday you go to bed three hours later because you are watching a movie or a TV series. So then you get up three hours later on Sunday... isn't that like jet lag to the body? Then, you expect to fall asleep Sunday evening at the same time and get up feeling refreshed Monday? Don't think so! I'm not saying be a monk, but if you are already complaining of being tired and exhausted and overworked and stressed... well then, some sacrifices may have to be made!

Second is to remove distractions... I've posted about this before. Try to take away distractions from sleep. There is probably some link between electronics and sleep – try to turn them off 30-odd mins before you sleep and not have them in the room. I can't say I have seen the data on it, but in theory, it makes sense to not stimulate the brain. Though, for some, like me, watching an episode of Friends before bed tends to switch off the brain from the day. What I now do, though, is a) not watch it in bed and b) have the night mode switched on. That's the best I can do for me now. I've tried reading, but the concentration is too much.

So there we have my first two sleep primers. As with anything that's good for you and needs changing, at first it's difficult, near on impossible, but after a while your habit changes, the system reboots and suddenly you reap the rewards.

#buildthechain

THURSDAY

June 21

What is an OUTCOME goal?

- A given weight loss goal
- 10% body fat
- Increased muscle mass
- Drop three dress sizes
- 100kg back squat

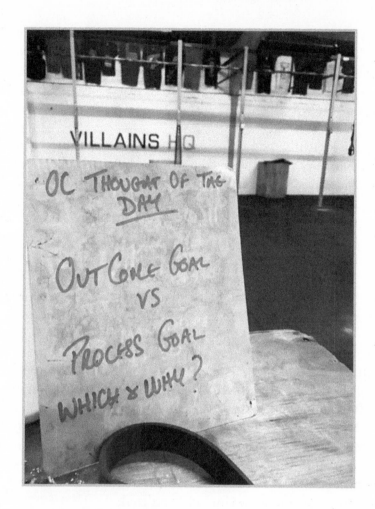

- A bodyweight deadlift
- Fran under 4 mins

What is wrong with an outcome goal? Nothing really, but it leaves an element of control down to other people, other factors... things YOU CANNOT CONTROL. Now, when setting goals you want to have the control, you want to have the 100% certainty that you can achieve them.

With any of the goals above, you CANNOT 100% say that you will achieve it. There are external forces, biology and mechanics that can stop you in your tracks! When I set you a goal, I want to know you can achieve it. It's my job to empower you and mitigate the risks, remove the obstacles… I want you to know that you CAN ACHIEVE!

Take wanting to lose 10kg… there are countless things that can get in the way of that.

1. Biologically, you cannot say for certainty that you can lose 10kg. As you move into a caloric deficit, your 'metabolism' can slow, you can lose muscle mass or you may increase muscle mass. These things can make it harder to drop than 10kg.

2. Sabotage! We've seen it time and time again. You want to lose 10kg but other people like you just the way you are. They offer you cakes, they take you out for lunch, they say you're doing well and then with the next sentence offer you a pudding.

As you can see, there are external forces at work, some of which you can't control. Biology is hard to control, and it's human behaviour not to disappoint, so when people are faced with saying 'NO' they often can't, and instead they say 'YES'.

Hitting a 50kg back squat… Again, we as coaches may know that you can 100% hit that goal, but again there are so many external factors at work. Mobility, movement barriers, technical flaws, mindset, slow twitch vs fast twitch muscle fibres… all these things can stop you achieving a lifting goal.

SO, WHAT DO I PREFER?
PROCESS goals!

I remember a phrase that goes 'no one force feeds you and no one other than you put food in your mouth' (unless you're a baby of course). You are in 100% control of that – no one else. (Note: there are some instances whereby you are given food by someone else, but the action of inserting it into your mouth is all you!) Process goals are goals that will help you hit your outcome goal, but they are things that IF YOU DO, you will be on the right path to your outcome goals.

Let me give you an example:

Your outcome goal is to lose 20kg... it's daunting, it's huge. However, switch the focus to process goals and the thing doesn't seem so daunting:

1. Change your nutrition to hitting a protein goal given to you to hit daily.
2. Eliminate junk foods from a list I give to my clients.
3. Turn up to training on the days agreed.
4. Do a weekly accountability session.

Taking these a bit further and being more specific...
Nutrition Goals:

1. I will hit 30g of protein in each of my meals.
2. I will only consume carbohydrates in my post-workout meal.
3. I will drink 1 litre of water by 9am.

These are examples of process goals. They are very easy to 'tick off', easily attainable and daily focused, and if done, would get you closer to your goal, if fat loss was the goal. If you completed these processes over a period of 10–30 days, do you think that they would help you attain the goal of fat loss, be it 10kg or get to 10%? YES, they would, but now the pressure and the sometimes disappointing method of standing on the scales on a weekly basis is eliminated. You have hit POSITIVE process goals, will be feeling healthier, be feeling stronger, be feeling more energetic, and will be leaner...

Now, hitting the goals is not easy. They still require work and effort, but they are smaller and more manageable. They are kept on a daily level and not a week by week basis, where everything rides on the scales at one moment in time when other factors could be at play. I've seen countless people's motivation crushed when I get an email or message saying they have been perfect but their weight hasn't budged. Yet, with a focus on the process instead of the outcome, they would be in a positive mindset and understand that the results will come from consistency in hitting the process goals. If you don't hit a goal one day, it is highlighted and you can do something about it, whereas with a weekly weigh-in there may be seven days of torture, not knowing, and the stress of that may move you off track.

Positive vs potentially negative goal setting...

Most people set goals in the new year... why not attack it now? Because of Xmas? Sounds like an excuse, a delay in taking ACTION! Be the person who stands up TODAY and takes action... 1 or 2kg between now and Xmas means that you're 1 or 2kg closer to your goal, and gives you that focus to get back in after Xmas off!

Want help setting goals? Let us know and we can help... more than happy. Change your focus now, set yourself up for success and positivity rather than disappointment. Trust in your coach's methods. Trust in yourself to hit those goals and go for it!

Go, get in touch now! #buildthechain

FRIDAY

June 22: REflection Friday.

REflection is a vital part of growth. Sitting down and looking at the last seven days gives you an overview of what went well and what needs work on.

So let's go through the three categories, shall we...

Training and nutrition

This week I was mature... by Wednesday I was spent. After a strength in depth qualifier that lasted under 5 mins on Monday, the adrenaline factor and effort left my body tired and lethargic. So, by Wednesday, I cut the volume, cut the training down going into a rest day and now the body feels much more capable of today's

workload. If you train you to learn about your body, you know true tiredness vs perceived tiredness. Use that to know when to back off in all forms of life.

Business

With summer coming, you get a lot of people enquiring about fitness... last-minute attempts to lose a few kgs and feel better about themselves. We've got some great trainers and staff, but our job as business owners is to make sure as many of these people as possible get the advice and opportunity to experience what proper, coached and applicable training looks like, and make sure we don't miss that opportunity by being lazy with our responses and sincere with our advice. Systems are good, but always need refining.

Home

When a child sleeps, it feels miraculous. It's also funny to think that a week ago I was reading very child-based stories to little OC and now we've moved on to (still a child's book) Harry Potter... which I learnt that JK Rowling is the first human ever to gross over 1 billion from a book series. A simply amazing statistic... who knew that this lady who got told she wasn't imaginative enough has created such a huge – scrap that – the world's biggest empire of fiction.

Have a great weekend... reflect and #buildthechain

Oscar did a doodle on my phone, which made me chuckle... Who knows, in 30 years' time he could be a famous artist and that might be worth millions...

MONDAY

June 25: Monday rambles is a training ramble...

'It's not the strongest of the species that survive, it's the most adaptable', said some very clever person.

Everyone thinks that more is better. Everyone thinks that physical changes happen the more you do... the more sets, the more weight, etc. However, while it's true on one front that over time the relative volume must increase to create overload and thus create adaptation, it's missing a huge chunk of the story.

When you learn something, you do it in blocks or stages. You don't learn a language, for example, by just being dumped a load of text and just expect to learn it. You break it down into volumes and stages which you can reap the most reward from. It's all about choosing the appropriate volume and getting the most from each stage.

The training I have for years got 'wrong'...

'ITS NOT THE STRONGEST OF THE SPECIES THAT SURVIVE, IT'S THE MOST ADAPTABLE.'

Sp Adobe Spark

I say 'wrong' because everything is a learning experience. We have (as Dr Mike Israetel writes) volume landmarks. These are volumes specific to us and our training age whereby if we train under them, we won't stimulate a change in the body, and if we train over them, we will overreach and likely be hampered by injuries and overuse symptoms... Guess which one I have used in the past?! We have both a systemic maximal recoverable volume (MRV) and a muscle group MRV. Anything over these and we risk injury but for very little reward. The sweet spot lies in the middle ground and can provide us with YEARS of progression in our physique and strength. Why try to train with 20 sets when you can get use from 12/14/16/18 sets... it's taken me a long time to realise that I don't need to do 20 sets of squats. I can do 12 in week 1 and feel recovered. The following week, I can do 13 or 14 and still feel recovered and probably able to increase the weight on the bar too. Week 3, I can do 14–16 sets and feel great but know I'm reaching capacity. Week 4... I would have previously prob gone to 20 sets... there's no need... not every time... that risks injury for me, it risks setbacks, especially with other life factors involved, like disrupted sleep and long days chasing clients and kids around. I can get more... from less. I'm learning to adapt. I'm not the strongest and I'm not the leanest, but I'm starting to adopt the more I learn, and that's the key. As the quote states above, it's not the strongest of the species that survive, it's the most adaptable.

Don't feel that more is always better. Instead, listen to your body and read the signs. Coaches can do that for you too... it's why I have certain questions in my feedback forms for nutrition and training. Any flu or cold symptoms? It's the first sign that something might be up with recovery – that and the muscle soreness lasting longer than normal. Pay attention to your body's signals... don't assume you can handle more, when you can get better on less!

It's a journey, with no set destination... #buildthechain

TUESDAY

June 26: Tuesday rambles...

Prescribing relaxation with activity!
By now, most people have heard of the 10,000 steps a day prescription for activity-based health. This 10k seems to be the aim of most people and probably is around about the right aim for most. This is a range, most likely, but it's certainly true that if you are looking at trying to become healthier and perhaps lose a bit of weight that increasing your steps by whatever you are doing now by 2000 will probably (if done consistently) be a great method, wouldn't it? The only problem is that this figure seems to stress people out. It's yet ANOTHER thing that they are trying to achieve on top of all the other stressful things that they are doing, like

Adobe Spark

training, nutrition, training, avoiding temptation, dealing with kids, more training, nutrition, etc. So, while we know it may be great for us, it can add to the stress pile, mentally more than physically... What I have found, though, is that with the right prescription, you can change it from a stress to an opportunity to RELAX!

Some options:

1. Music. Is there anything nicer than putting on a set of headphones and wandering along listening to your favourite songs? Hell, you can even find somewhere in the countryside and sing along at the top of your lungs. Walk, listen, sing... revisit old songs from the past. We don't get that opportunity much nowadays... seize the chance.

2. Listen to a book. In the three weeks, I've listened to two books I've wanted to read for about two years. Granted, I don't think I've taken in as much as I would if I'd read them, because you get distracted by a car or a thought and before you know it you are hitting the 15s rewind button 20 times.

3. Listen to a podcast. There are podcasts on EVERY subject now. Literally. From Fearne Cotton interviewing Stephen Fry on mental health, to Louie Simmons talking about accommodating resistance... from the gut and its influence on mental health, to Derek Woodske's EcoBolic Radio talking about the past and the future of strength and conditioning, to laughing at your favourite comedian being interviewed. It's amazing to be able to hear this information at the touch of a button for FREE.

As you can see, you can turn this potentially stressful 'Go for a walk and get your steps up' to a huge opportunity to relax, learn, wonder, and think about subjects that you don't get the opportunity to usually... Or you can sing and dance along like no one's watching and just keep putting one foot in front of the other.

Life's a journey, #buildthechain

THURSDAY

June 28: Thursday rambles.

Five easy action steps that will bring you the body you want!

1. Eat protein at every meal.
2. Start the day with a new habit.

5 THINGS TO TAKE YOU CLOSER TO YOUR GOALS

Sp Adobe Spark

3. Get hydrated.
4. Be the tortoise, but champion the hare.
5. Be prepared.

Let me expand a little on each one:

1. Protein. Boring as this is, and probably also overused as a piece of advice, it does as a basic approach make a lot of sense. As you can see, this step is first or of primary importance. Protein is simply the building blocks of our body. We cannot survive without it. We need it to recover from exercises, and we need it to lay down new tissue and cells.

Simply put, those who do not get enough of it, will never reach their full potential.

2. Start the day with a new habit in mind – and that's the key, IN MIND. You see, when you start a new habit or decide on a new habit, you are bringing it into your consciousness. The more you think of something, the more likely it is that you will do it.

Habits work well when linked with other activities. While the 'anabolic window' may be irrelevant, it can be useful to request a shake after a workout. So, they remember... workout>shake, just as an example. (The shake's not the point, the link is.)

Your 'bad' habits will never disappear. The opposite good habit will get stronger and stronger, but realising that your bad habit never dies will help take the pressure off.

An example could be writing down how long you slept for. It highlights an important habit, and fixes in your mind the importance of it.

3. It's the most BORING thing in nutrition, but drinking enough water genuinely is also probably the most under-rated habit you are not doing! From a cellular level, nothing functions optimally without optimal hydration. Performance wise, again your performance will be hugely capped if you are not drinking enough water. On a recovery level, you cannot recover from sessions if you don't have the water in your body to lubricate and carry nutrients in and out of cells and every system in your body. We are virtually made up of the stuff... a 1% drop is catastrophic to your results! While it's hot out at the moment, try dropping some essential amino acids into the bottle for a bit of flavour and a wee bit of extra protein.

4. So everyone knows the story of the hare and the tortoise. While it's good to take it slow and steady and think the long game, sometimes you need to take risks, sometimes you need to accelerate. Some of the most successful people in history took huge risks and failed many times over, but guess what... that one time it comes off can have the biggest

reward ever! Be the tortoise but sometimes champion and trust your gut... go with the fast pace and learn lessons from your failures and make them your strengths! The next time the hare runs that race, he may just sprint, rest, sprint, rest and cross that line well ahead of the tortoise!

5. Fail to prepare, prepare to fail. This is crucial in nutrition, training, finances, life... everything. The more prepared you are for any situation, the better placed you are to succeed. Nutrition for me is all about getting the things in place to allow you to succeed. How to cook, take a lesson, what tools do you need... you can bulk cook if you have a 17-foot frying pan and a plastic spoon. Catch my drift? You need to do the groundwork to set yourself up for the greatest return.

There you have five things that may just help you bring the body you want one or ten steps closer. Have a great day, and as always, get in touch when you need our help!

#buildthechain

FRIDAY

June 29: Reflection Friday.

Usually on a Friday I reflect on the week. However, today while driving in, I heard a great podcast in which they were talking about reactions vs responses. This, I think, will help with the nutritional side of things, training, competing and generally in life too.

Reactions are emotional knee-jerks, instant decisions. They often are immediate, spontaneous and often not thought through.

Responses, however, are measured, thought through... principles are applied and strategic.

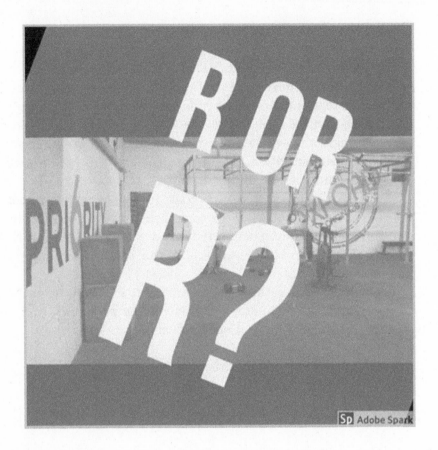

In life, this may come as simply as... you get to the gym, it's been a long day, maybe you've hit traffic too, you unpack your gym bag and bang... no training shoes. To react might be to curse and storm out 'can't is arsed with this today'. The response-based action might be to ask around and see if there are any spares, or to talk to the coaching staff, explain the situation and ask if you can train barefoot, or to change training and find a quiet spot and run through some mobility and core work.

One reaction is emotional and unhelpful, while one response is measured and thought out. I'm not saying that in every situation a reaction isn't warranted... sometimes it is. But generally speaking, if we chose the response method, we could reduce our stress, stay in control and see more clearly.

Traffic is a great example. I've said it before, you can't help traffic on the road, you get stuck in it. The response for me is...

'great more learning time'... A reaction, but not my reaction, would be to curse.

In a competition in CrossFit, your skipping rope breaks mid-workout. The reaction might be tears and throwing it down in disgust and just sitting there. My response, however, would be (depending on the workout), after the person is done doing their routine next to you, ask them if you can grab their rope, and carry on. Next, ask a supporter in the crowd, wait calmly and concentrate on the breathing, rest. You can't do anything about it, other than come back into the workout with heart rate controlled and just get as many reps in as possible. Alternatively, even before this ever happens, you could have prepared for this moment... you could have taken two ropes onto the floor. Preparing for anomalies and worst-case scenarios quite often set the champions of any field apart from the others. Michael Phelps trained with water-filled goggles in case it happened during a race, which meant that when it did happen, he knew his response... maybe taking two ropes out there isn't the worse idea?

It's very, very hard to respond rather than react. I think it's a learnt trait over time. I think, as a child, I reacted, and over time I've learnt to try to respond. Especially with an underlying ADHD, you never know what the reaction might be, so it's taken time and I'm by no means good at it. All the things above are responses I'm writing about while not in the actual situation... I hope I would have had the mental fortitude to respond rather than react.

So next time you are faced with a decision to make, perhaps at a restaurant and you are trying to lose some weight, do you react or do you respond? When faced with a change in programming, do you react and throw your teddies out the cot because you prepared for one thing rather than another, or do you accept it and see the benefits? When you're handed a new project at work and you're already struggling, do you react or do you respond?

I thought it was a useful podcast... my response was to share it. Have a great Friday, have a great weekend.

#buildthechain

MONDAY

July 2: Monday ramble in the woods – bit deep this one!

Time... the most valuable thing we can't buy more of.

What do you do with your time?

Here's a thought. I'm 33 – if I'm average, I'm going to live to about 81.6 years. That means I've got 49 summers left. Now there's a head f**k for you! Think I'm going to waste a second of that on negativity and not pour all my energy and attention into love and creating memories?!

Not only that, but for most people they pretty much stop being able to do stuff when they are 60–70. At 60, a lot of people start the decline into ageing. Screw that! Past 70, and as the muscle mass drops because of the lack of movement, the ability to get up and go decreases. Sod that!

There are multiple reasons why I place such a high value on health and fitness… every single one of those summers I have left, I'm going to LIVE it, make a memory, improve my craft, leave a mark on someone's life, and continue to build a legacy, be it through my children or through the vehicle of our business.

As I walk through the woods today, I count myself very, very lucky that I have potentially 49 summers (I plan on making it more, as I'm not average… I know more than the average to keep my health and heart beating longer). I know that over time my training will have to change to accommodate the physiological changes of ageing. I know that to increase life expectancy things change, but I know that path. I'll share those things, so that someone else too can benefit from a few extra summers!

Ever feel like your goals aren't worth achieving? Well, take 82 minus your age and see how long you have left. If that doesn't inspire you to be the very best version of you so that you can live a better, happier, more confident life… then I don't know what will!

#buildthechain

P.S. interested in longevity and health into your 40s and beyond? Get in touch, let's talk, let's put you on a better path… the commitment to your health is a lot simpler than you think and a lot less than you perceive!

TUESDAY

July 3

Tuesday rambles from the countryside... early dog walk! (Look after your pets, people – get that walk in early if it's hot!)

The power of the group. There's nothing more powerful than a tribe... think about it, the power is in the collective. No singular person is more powerful than pulling in and harnessing the power of multiple people.

Take business... it grows faster when you hire others.

In fitness the group brings motivation, the group brings accountability, the group brings out the best! Over the last 24+ years of either competitive sport or fitness training, the most obvious thing to me is that a team or group brings out far more results than doing it on your own. So why is it people think that they will succeed in health and fitness by themselves? It just doesn't make sense. Just doesn't!

Why do we have group training as our main focus in P6? ... because it works! The power is in the group. Mix in our knowledge and programming, mix in coaching and cues, add in a sprinkle of laughter and perhaps some nutritional advice, and results are inevitable. The coaches often have their best training sessions too when we train in threes or more... the energy is higher, the accountability to push is higher.

Take-away from today: if you struggle with motivation and accountability, join a tribe, a group or collective with the same goals that fit your times, More on that tomorrow... 'time' the biggest excuse we hear in hitting goals! Build that chained person – every day add a link, so that minimum thing for maximum return. One step, one at a time, don't skip a step!

#buildthechain

WEDNESDAY

July 4

For Wednesday rambles we revisit our hashtags meaning... the concept of Building the Chain.

It's a great way to stay on the right track, and this theme is used by our gym to hold you accountable to yourself and keep you on track.

It all starts with your goals – your outcome goals. Write them out: Lose 20lbs for example.

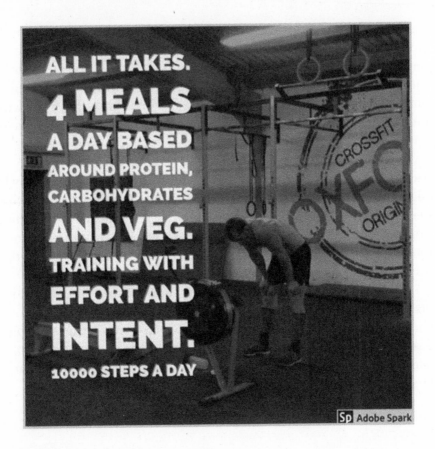

Now, you actually have little control over the number... you can't say for sure how long it will take and whether that figure will make you happy.

But what you do next WILL have an effect on your life for the positive. You will feel happier and more in control of your life.

Write out the habits and processes which you need to hold daily in order to get you to your goal.

- Eat four meals a day, consisting of lean protein, carbohydrates from XYZ sources, two to three servings of veg, etc. This is easily definable and easy to say whether you achieved or didn't.
- Go to the gym three days a week (preferably to a class or scheduled coached session... research shows you train harder and get better results).
- Hit 10,000 steps a day.

- Introduce three daily habits that will build confidence, are easy to quantify and are habits for a lifetime.
- Now buy either a wall or book calendar of a whole year. Have your habits written out above it and stick it up on the wall.

Each day you do the processes by which you achieve your goals, put a BIG green X through the day. Right now, it should be easy to hit those Xs. Your aim is to NOT BREAK THE HABIT CHAIN!

The habit chain is a powerful concept – it puts you in charge, it gives you a visual representation of your commitment to yourself. Do you really want to break that chain? I guarantee that once you see 10 days in a row of big GREEN Xs, you're going to think twice about unbooking that class or choosing takeaway over your nutrition plan... Ask yourself, DO YOU REALLY WANT TO BREAK THE HABIT CHAIN? It's powerful because it hands YOU the CHOICE to make or break your goal in a visual and easy to see way!

'But Ollie, what happens if I do succumb and the chain is broken?'... Simple, you write the number of days you managed to chain together in the day you go to... Next, you call or message your coach and then you identify why... Then you, here's the important part, MOVE ON and try to better the chain... beat your last run. You are not a bad person for having a slip-up, but what you do after defines your personality and commitment to what you want to achieve. Those who achieve greatness and their ambitions are those who see that slip-up, learn from it and move on. What if you are not currently being coached by a coach? Simple... reach out. All you have to do is contact and I will try, where I can, to help you through the issue.

Go out and buy a wall chart and let's see who can have the longest habit chain...

I guarantee that the person with the longest chain will be the person with the greatest results!

#buildthechain

THURSDAY

July 5: Thursday rambles on a dog walk...

Lessons from an athlete. Athletes are judged, not always on just their performance but, ultimately, they are. If you don't win, you are often labelled as a failure... I stopped being an athlete in the simple sense a long time ago because I learnt that I enjoyed the process of training more than the judgement of winning.

Training makes you a better person... winning doesn't. It's the grind, the struggle, the overcoming of something you previously couldn't do...

Training goes deeper than physique, strength, etc – it's a lifestyle of positivity, an expression of improvement. Vast improvement... you can't see that anywhere else in life, I don't think. I can't think of any situation where you can see regular improvement across so many variables, with such regularity. Even better, you have COMPLETE CONTROL of it. That's a beautiful thing... 100% your control, you choose to do it, you focus on it. Failure isn't present unless you give up. Everything else is successful – just turning up, just lifting, moving, smiling and embracing your body and its abilities... then you simply improve, day by day.

The pressures for perfection come externally... the media etc portray an image of perfection (which, by the way, is impossible, as it's an opinion). The beauty of fitness and health is that there is only the process of improvement. No one actually knows how far you or I can take their physical and mental well-being and performance.

This, in itself, can wreak havoc in someone's mind, as there is no endpoint. Once you reach a goal, another appears... you will never be done. Here's the new plan:

- Seek improvement DAILY.
- Seek to install new positive habits and thoughts into your mind.
- Seek to be the leader in your own life.

Simply put, put the BEST version of yourself out to the world.

#buildthechain

FRIDAY

July 6: REflection Friday.

Training... a hugely positive week. The first week of a programme I believe is all about finding the starting weights, tweaking the exercise order and an exercise selection based on current injuries or progressions. This week I got it right and was also surprised by some of the weights moved. It's amazing when you take your time with progression and don't rush how it all comes together. There's the message: you don't have to rush!

Business... we've got some exciting things in the pipeline to hopefully expand our reach in the local community. That, and we've chosen things to challenge us mentally and physically. Summer is an interesting time in the fitness industry. The coming together of a plan is a fantastic feeling though.

Family... fun, laughter, play, humour – all of these have been at play. As a parent it's a constant learning curve. They do have books on it, but they are dry and boring. We live and we learn. I'm on a constant quest to be the best dad, father, daddy I can be... it's a hard balance to find, but that's the fun. There's no manual for life, no perfection, just enjoyment, learning and growth!

The rambles this week have touched on a few things, the most poignant being, I think, the concept of chasing progress rather than perfection.

Reflect back on the week, look for the positive steps, seek improvement in areas of weakness, be honest and open. Everyone has something to offer this world... you just have to start believing it.

#buildthechain

MONDAY

July 9

Monday rambles on a slightly cooler morning... wiping spiders' webs from my face every 2 secs!

Want the simplest way to be all you want to be? Physically, emotionally, mentally...

- Write down the person you want to be.
- Seek out the method to get there, the values and beliefs that need to be in place.
- Have someone hold you accountable, and now live up to those expectations.

Adobe Spark

Simple, huh?

ABSOLUTELY NOT!

It's a lifelong project, one where you will question yourself, question why, give up multiple times to realise you need it. You will hate it... but you will:

- Be more confident
- Have self-respect
- Be happier
- Have friends who value your opinion
- Live a healthy and long life, proud of what you have become

- Be respected
- Be spoken of highly
- Have control of your life
- Be a role model
- Stress less because you know how to handle it

But you will need help, you will need to be open and honest, you will need to make mistakes, you will need to open your mind to the fact you don't have all the answers, you will need to reflect often, you will seek improvement at all opportunities, you will need to fight when you want to crawl into a dark hole and sleep away the pain, you will have to suffer to realise all the happiness you have, you will need to welcome new people into your life, you will be uncomfortable regularly, you will conquer fears, and you will feel massively uncomfortable doing that.

Basically, in this game of self-improvement, you will have to go through a lot of unrest to achieve. The journey is not the destination, rather it's the stories along the way. The most interesting people I've ever met or studied aren't those who had it simple... they are instead the ones who overcame adversity and had to work through character traits that worked against them. The story makes the triumph, not the outcome.

So, this Monday, what's your story going to be? Do you slay the dragon after a shit storm of quests and boobytraps... or do you just set off on a flat road with no excitement and slay it in its sleep?

I'm taking it head on. I've failed more times than I can remember, but I learn each time. I get back up, reflect and then move with purpose, determined not to make the same mistakes again.

Make your story #buildthechain

TUESDAY

July 10: Tuesday rambles around a countryside track, watching a pointer run wild!

Have you ever tried negative motivation?

Here's a weird one I've never really considered. The theory is based off my observation of some really successful people in sport, in business and in life.

We constantly seek positivity in life and a feeling of self-worth, but a lot of the very successful people in the world have overcome negativity and hatred... it inspires them to do and be more.

So is there a proportion of the population who need negativity in order for them to produce their best?

In a workout, for example, if someone was to say 'you can't lift that, you're not strong enough, you're rubbish' and basically smack talk you, would you believe them or would you use that negativity as fuel to the fire and prove them wrong?

We, as coaches, are always trying to bring out the best in our members and training partners, so what if during a qualifying workout in the CrossFit Open (a yearly event in which you compete against people in five given workouts testing all manner of fitness modalities), you actively smack talked your athletes, rather than encouraged them? There must be a proportion of people who would actually perform better than through the usual 'Come on Bob, you're doing awesome, keep going, move, move, move'. From the outside, it would seem very odd, and some people looking in would see it as a very odd thing, but we are all different... we are motivated by different means. One person's gold is another's poison.

It's definitely something I'd like to see applied and see what happens. I steer clear of negativity so much that maybe I'm missing some performance-related gains, so to speak. I know I perform when the pressure is on, so I know that stress actually activates a self-competitive element in me. I know I perform my best work when the outcome is out of my control and I can stand proud knowing that nothing more could have been given in that moment of time. Maybe though, just maybe, someone saying 'you can't do that, you're not good enough'... maybe that, to some, might be the key to unlocking some untapped potential deep inside them.

Have a great Tuesday. Perhaps today, reach out to someone you haven't spoken to in a while, maybe just ask what's been going on in their life... be a chain builder, be someone else's positivity, make someone's day.

#buildthechain

WEDNESDAY

July 11, Wednesday rambles.

Wednesday rambles on a cooler day, being covered in spiders' webs while walking down country tracks.

We can't change what we aren't aware of...

Self-growth isn't easy. Often there are hurdles and obstacles in the way, but most of them you actually aren't even aware of. It's like that hole in the wall you pass by in your house every day – after a while, you don't even notice it's there.

Those holes may have been there years in your chain. One of the most difficult tasks I think someone could undertake is to sit down with a friend or collective and simply ask... 'What am I not good at?'

You are asking those people to make you aware of the things that are there for the world to see that you can't. Remember, though, this is a positive exercise... it's not there to bash you, but instead it's there to make you aware of those things, so that you are able to implement change and work on them. Maybe you need help with those things, maybe you need educating in those areas. Learning after you leave school becomes interesting. For 10–15 years of schooling and university, you pretty much loathe learning... you get told what you need to learn about, exams happen and that's it. You now have the opportunity to learn about things in your adult life that interest you, that can help you succeed, and that make you a better person.

When you learn, you immediately improve – an instant upskills. If it was a computer game, for example, you just levelled up. In order to learn, you need to be aware... you need to know... where the least amount of time can bring the greatest return.

The greatest leaders know their weaknesses and plug the holes with learning and with someone who can do a better job than them. The greatest people know their faults and work on them, but focus on what they have to give to the friends and family they have around them and the mission they are on. Don't be afraid to ask for help. There are people who have done and been through the hard work for you... they have educated themselves to make your journey easier than theirs.

At school, myself being an ADHD wizard, I had huge problems with timekeeping and being where I was meant to be. I was made aware of this by my Latin teacher, Mr. Brisbane. He sat me down after a Latin quiz, which I nailed, as I actually loved Classics. He said, 'Ollie, you know, you're actually a good student... you have potential, but your organisation and timekeeping is awful.'

    Mr. B: 'Have you got your diary?'
      OC: 'I've lost it, sir.'
    Mr. B: 'Well, there's the first problem. Let's get another one.'
Out he went and came back with a diary.

He spent the next 15–20 mins showing how he, as an ultra-organised person, had his diary organised into colour coding and times. Wherever a time was indicated, his aim was to be 5 mins early. There were different colours for different events and priorities. Nowadays, it's gone from the Sandroyd School calendar to an A5 diary, to iCal, but all still colour coded, and always 5 mins early.

To this day, I still value that life lesson and continue to use its principles. He's probably unaware that his identification and my lack of awareness of my organisational skills were leading me to suffer in other areas.

Be open to being made aware!
#buildthechain

THURSDAY

July 12

The 10,000-hour rule... but with a purpose! My take on this well-known 'rule'.

Everyone has heard that to master something, you need to put in 10,000 'repetitions' or hours of time into that field... but if you put in crappy practice, you'll get a crappy return! So, here's a more specific version for you to ponder.

The magic lies in how the 10,000 hours are spent and how they are performed... the intent and the purpose. You have to focus on things that you don't know how to do, not on the things you're already proficient at. I've been pondering the fact that I've now spent over 10 years in the fitness industry. In that time, every day I have performed anywhere between 0 and 10 coaching sessions per day (yes, some days I do have off). I've studied at least 30–60 mins every day, and I've immersed myself in this industry

Adobe Spark

of health, wellness and fitness. I've accrued well over those 10,000 hours... prob quadruple that... and you know what? ... every day there's something new to learn, something to develop, something to master. My view is that you never master anything – you may be the best there is, but as a master of it, you would realise that you haven't mastered it at all.

You can, however, be the best you can be and strive for more, so when undertaking those tasks, think about what practices would give you the greatest return on your investment (time). It's based off a bookmark I'd put in a Chasing Excellence audible... loving listening to some books right now that I just haven't had the time to read.

You need to undertake the tasks that are deliberately designed to improve performance. You must always practise the basics, but to become great at something, you need to learn things in those areas that you don't know or that you are not good at. It has to be methodical and specific to improving the things you can't already do!

You need to repeat that task A LOT. Once identified you need to practise it repeatedly, over and over. Movement is something we take for granted. If you have a crappy movement patterned ingrained... then to undo it requires countless repetition in the new and improved movement.

You need feedback on results and it needs to be continuously available. You need to be able to receive feedback that allows you to either see improvement or see fault, so that you can improve further. As yesterday's post said, 'You can't improve what you are not aware of.' Coaches, videos, examinations, tests... these things are feedback mechanisms.

Improvement is highly demanding mentally and sometimes it's not going to be enjoyable. This is probably due to the fact you are improving areas that are currently underdeveloped and therefore slow going. Sometimes those hours may seem not worth it. There's nothing wrong at that stage in taking a break and coming back refreshed with a new perspective. In the fitness profession, I've seen a few trainers get frustrated with the industry, take a sabbatical and come back better for it. I've seen athletes take a break from their sport to come back stronger. It will suck sometimes – 10,000 hours is a long time. No shame in looking elsewhere for inspiration and renewed purpose.

There you have it. The other thing that makes these 10,000 hours more fun and have a purpose is to see the enjoyment from the process, now that you're heading towards something that does bring you enjoyment.

#buildthechain

THURSDAY

July 12: Thursday rambles of a fitness fanatic.

It's been reported that 13% of people enjoy what they do for a living!

This stat blows my mind!

That means there's 87% of people out there who dislike at least eight hours of the day. Assuming they sleep eight, that's 33% of the day they don't enjoy. If they spend 33% of the day asleep... the other 33% is shared between cooking, eating, dressing, procrastinating.

No wonder a) people are suffering more and more from mental health diseases, and b) taking shortcuts in their lives in terms of convenience foods.

In a day where you can, in fact, change careers and jobs fairly easily, it does make you wonder if in the future we will see more people follow their passion and enter a different workspace.

I said to myself a long time ago I'm unemployable... simply for the fact that I have too many ideas and dreams about what is possible. I can't be mentally leashed. I need the feeling of freedom to create and set up. This world of fitness is perfect for that – there are countless combinations of programmes to write, some working for some, but not for others. Nutrition is simple, but as you develop as a coach, you realise the complexity is multifaceted and you are fighting against years of habits, media and preconceived ideas. Skills are developed in communication and language along the way. Then there's the business world of fitness, the transition to online marketing and the creativity that comes with it.

I'm one of the 13% who like their work. In fact, of that 13%, there are probably fewer who love what they do. I'm also fairly sure that as time goes on, the role will change and the emphasis will shift, niching down even further. I'm also surrounded by talent, and I think that quite often, they don't realise how talented they are.

If you're struggling in life, look at the areas you can change and influence. Eight of those hours a day for 50-odd years are changeable... you can influence them and you can change your path. I'm not saying quit your job and recklessly jump in, but look at the idea, explore it and plan it. Find someone who can help you plan that. For any of my ideas, I can see the path it could take me down. I plan how a day would look, I plan the timeline and I then beta test by asking people I trust what they think.

So, 33% of your time... I think you should start to enjoy it. When my kids grow up, I'll actively encourage them not to seek wealth in terms of money and possessions. Sure, they can want nice things, but I'll first encourage them to do something they enjoy for the next 70+ years. Whatever 'job' that is, they may get enjoyment from dancing to computer science or from food preparation to singing. I'll encourage them to find something within that space and go 100% all in on it. Then I'll help them stay accountable to that goal... when it doesn't look like it's going well, I'll help them stay on course. When they make it, I'll encourage them to carry on ticking the boxes, keep turning up and continue sharing the enthusiasm and their uniqueness in the world.

#buildthechain

MONDAY

July 16: Rambles with a pointer – beat the log book!

Want to know the simplest way to improve weekly, concentrate on your own self-development and learn to love the process? This was probably the origins of the Build the Chain process... at least, it's the area of my own personal journey where I saw the power of it first!

Firstly, you need a training diary... so many people stumble at that block. Unfortunately, your head doesn't count. We need to see it, feel it and have a physical presence in which to record and monitor. So grab a diary – you'll thank me for it.

You can now begin to progress in a more accountable way. It's a simple process really. Most training follows a 3- or 4-week programme where the variables don't change much: same reps and sets, or maybe an increase in volume via one of these being changed. The exercises usually stay the same. The task is simple... each week your aim is to beat what you did last week.

Say week one you lunged at body weight. Perfect, great start. Next week, when you come to that same Monday session, your body needs added stimulus. Everyone has heard the phrase: 'Do the same, remain the same.' So, the simplest thing to do is BEAT THE LOG BOOK – your mentality now is each

How To Never Remain The Same

Exercise	Reps	Tempo				Rest	WGT	RE
BB Back				1	0	30		
T Bar Row				1	0	30		
Leg Curl Plantarflexed	4	8-10	3	0	1	0	30	
Flat DB Press	4	8-10	3	0	1	0	90	
Alternating DB Lunge		-15	3	0	1	0	30	
Lat Pull Down Pronated Wide G		-15	3	0	1	0	30	
Clean Grip RDL		12-15	3	0	1	0	30	
DB Shoulder Press	4	12-15	3	0	1	0	90	

DAY 2- MST

Exercise	Sets	Reps	Tempo				Rest	WGT	REPS
Farmers Deadlift	10	20/2reps/20steps	2	0	X	0	IGYG		
Sled Push	10	20s	X	X	X	X	IGYG		
Assault Bike	10	20s	X	X	X	X	IGYG		
KB Swing	10	20s	X	X	X	X	IGYG		
Bear Crawl	10	20s	1	0	1	0	IGYG		

Day 3- Total Body GBC

Exercise	Sets	Reps	Tempo				Rest	WGT	REPS
Deadlift	4	8-10	3	0	1	0			
Seated Cable Row									

Adobe Spark

session to beat what you did the time before. Say you held the 3kg dumbbells... over the course of 3 sets of 10 lunges on each leg, you have moved 360kg more than your last session! That's incredible! You try to move 360kg in one... virtually impossible, except for a very few. You have accomplished something great by that improvement.

Therein lies the real amazing thing about fitness. It's not about how much you lift or who's the strongest, weirdly that's not what I find impressive. What I find impressive is the improvement, the effort, the mindset of change. From the consistency of beating your log book comes the result. Our bodies adapt to stimulus, not the thought of it or jumping ahead. They undergo change from being constantly tweaked and challenged... the very same message of our Build the Chain brand. Those small links all add up. If you continued to add 3kg to each dumbbell over four weeks, you'd end on the 9kg dumbbells. That's 1080kg lifted more than your starting lunges... that's going to create change, and you'll hardly even notice it, as you've done it in a progressive manner. If, after week one, you went straight to the 9s, you'd probably struggle – you may even not be able to do one set. Where does that leave you... upset, annoyed, questioning? Trust the process, beat your logbook, or at least aim to. If you don't, you may just be close to your maximum that day, but you live to fight another.

So, this Monday has had a look back in your training diary, to see what you did last week... aim to beat it, self-improvement. Focus on you. You control you, you decide your process.

#buildthechain

TUESDAY

July 17: Rambles in the woods again!

Using your fitness mentality in EVERY aspect of your life.
CrossFit has both a good and bad reputation. I think the time is coming, though, where the boxes left are attracting, or being set up by, some fantastic coaches, and thus the perceived weakness of CrossFit is being lost.

What's left is the hardest working, most self-improving family of fitness people you will meet.

Jason Khalifa is one of the most successful athletes and businessmen within the world of CF. He has become a master of taking elements of functional fitness and applying them to his life. One of the philosophies in CrossFit is the AMRAP... as many rounds as possible. When you look at the root of it, the AMRAP basically

concentrates all your effort into a manageable body of time with no distractions. For example, you may have a workout that's:

10-min AMRAP

- 10 squats
- 10 press-ups
- 200m row

So, in simple English, do those three exercises for 10 mins and do as many rounds as you can.

Simple.

What Jason has done is take that same system and applied it to life.

Grab a clock, set a timer, focus on ONE task and put your best effort into it. When the time runs out, you're done. Next task.

There's something about working against the clock. Remember back to school days or university... exams were basically an AMRAP. University, with deadlines looming – still you always left studying to the night before, right?

Try it in your place of work today. Want to clear your emails? Set a timer for 15 mins: 3, 2, 1 GO! You have 15 mins to get your emails done. That's it – focus and move!

I've tried it and love it. Having that timer acts as a reminder to stay on track, to get the work done and to stay on track. In a workout of 10 mins, like the above, you think solely about the reps... you don't think of your shopping list, your kids, your bad day. No, you focus because it's only 10 min, and you're trying to get as much done as possible. You're going to be super focused and diligent at getting the work done. It's going to bring a whole new world of productivity to your life.

So today, somewhere in your life, be it work, meal prep (a little bit like that old show Can't Cook, Won't Cook), your workout or your playtime with the kids, do the same thing. Set the timer, and do as many rounds as possible... Disclaimer: the only area I can see this being an issue, is driving... don't go amrap'ing your driving and then blame the ramblings!

Anyway, enjoy the day and seek out positivity... and thanks, Jason, for spreading yours!

#buildthechain

WEDNESDAY

July 18

Wednesday rambles... an important one for goal setters. This came up with a client yesterday, and she naturally had come

to the same conclusion, but now has a visual method by which to understand it.

It's the Circle of Control.
It's simple, as all great things are.

Two circles. In the first, all those things YOU are in control of.

- Your actions
- Your values
- Your ability to turn up
- Your hands
- Your words
- And more

All the things above are what you control. I like the saying, 'No one else puts food in your mouth.'
It's your action and one you are in control of.
In the other circle, the things that you have no control over ... all the other aspects.

- Outcome goal
- Others' thoughts

- Other actions
- Others' mistakes
- Others' jealously
- Traffic
- Weather
- Stock markets
- House prices

In Covey's book 'The 7 Habits of Highly Effective People', he came to the conclusion that those who were highly successful focused more on what they could influence rather than on the outcome or things they couldn't.

Inside the circle is everything you have control of.

Outside, everything you don't have control of, now serves no purpose.

The most important thing to know is that when you fully focus on the things you can control, great things happen! Not only that, but when you do, a translocation happens as you INFLUENCE all those things within the out-of-control circle. Your actions and your words can affect the thoughts and actions of others... you have the power.

Your habits and your actions put you in the best place possible in order to achieve the outcome goals you set for yourself.

Let's talk about real-world clients.

This person wants to achieve a 65kg snatch and an 80kg clean and jerk – those numbers are the outcome. We have no idea if they are doable (FYI I'm not coaching the Olympic lift, but looking after the nutritional side of things, which usually delves into mindset... they pretty much come hand in hand). We think they are achievable and we've got no reason to believe that they are not, though they are tough numbers to hit. Occasionally, you may go through times of questioning if an outcome goal is achievable, because you've never been there. So what do we focus on? We focus on the things we can control:

- Our nutrition
- Our recovery methods, like when we go to bed
- Our training, turning up
- Our approach to the bar

- Our warm-ups
- Our sticking to the programme
- Our trust
- Our communication by the words we speak and the actions we take

In other words, we put our effort into the things we can control, and we enjoy and focus on the processes by which to get there. Ultimately, if we are going to hit that goal, it's going to come through the dedication to our own actions, so you may as well focus on them rather than on the number. You learn a lot more by looking at yourself than by looking at others. You can only influence the outcome through your own actions. From there, what will be, will be. You achieve, sooner or later.

> Try the exercise.
> Two circles
> All those things you control
> Those you don't

Now focus on the shit that actually MATTERS. You know, that stuff YOU just identified as the things you control...

#buildthechain

THURSDAY

July 19: Thursday rambles.

Not often I follow on from a rambles on the same topic, but yesterday's post sparked some discussion both on social media and in person.

What happens if you do concentrate your mind on the things you cannot control...

When you are ruled by the things you can't control, a few things can happen and I'll try to give an example. They may seem minute and silly, but they are examples nonetheless.

Performance suffers.

Someone who concentrated on the external, the things they can't control, would be affected by things like the weather. Golf might be an example. So many golfers suffer in the wind and rain. You can go into that round thinking you're going to play crap... your performance will already suffer. Not only that, but you tend to forget that the conditions are the same for every person on that course! The external conditions do not control the path of your club, they don't make the decision for you... you decide how to play that shot. Then you learn from it.

Yesterday it was hot. I was working out... 20–1 Ski Erg and DB clean and jerks. In the round of 19s, it dawned on me I'd forgotten my drink. It was in the next room – I realised I'd forgotten it. The thoughts went through my head: do I go and get it, stop the workout, come back and jump back in, or do I use it as a learning experience? Conditions won't always be perfect... I won't have my drink to hand, I'll feel a little rank, I'll want a sip. But I thought to myself, use it as an opportunity to practise in conditions that are unfavourable, which in the future I might experience. I'm just a dad trying to be the best version of myself for my family. I had nothing riding on it, but the principles are ingrained.

Ben Bergeron speaks of the CrossFit Games being a perfect example of where athletes prepare the best they can but are thrown curve balls where they get flown to a ranch in sizzling heat, told to do a trial run into another workout, then flown back, get a crap night's sleep, and told to perform on only four hours sleep. Some succumbed to the external, but in the case of his athletes, trained in mindset and positivity, they focused on the internal, the things they could control... their actions, their thoughts, their mindset. Low and behold, Katrina and Mat won the Games.

Away from performance, when you tend to focus on the things out of your control... others' thoughts, others' actions, others' skills and talents... it really only leads to anxiety and potentially depression. These people tend to always compare themselves to others. It's a dangerous game to always be looking at others and comparing yourself, as humans tend to only look at others' strengths and our own imperfections. Well, this might be the right time to drop in that statement that 'Perfection is a flawed concept and impossible to achieve'. You can only be you. You compare yourself and doubt yourself usually on the basis of no real evidence. Usually, the thing that holds us back in our lives is ourselves... it's not anyone else. It's our own mindset and inability to see our own worth, talent and place in the world. I cannot stress enough the importance of focusing on yourself and the things you can control. It's one of the most liberating lessons I have learnt, to know that all the power, all the choices, all that I have to come is a direct result of what I WANT TO HAPPEN. Others can influence it, but ultimately what I see is what I decide. If I focus my thoughts on self-improvement, on being a master of my own values and habits, it can only lead to a much, much better life, one where I'm the best version of myself at that moment in time. What good am I to those I love if I don't put forwards my best self? It's not easy to switch over to this way of thinking, and it may take years. A lot of us have a past that affects us, but over time, with practice, change is possible if you want it. That goes for anything in life, but ultimately it still starts with YOU!

#buildthechain

It's the Circle of Control.
It's simple, as all great things are.

Two circles. In the first all those things YOU are in control of:

- Your actions
- Your values

...

OUTRO

The process is never complete, and as daunting as that may be, there's great fun in that. I hope this book has shown you, at least, a part of what the world has to offer if you're willing to think about it in a different way.

We have this one opportunity whereby we can perceive our life as great and meaningful, or we can live our lives conforming to how society believes we should be. I challenge myself daily to be better, better at something, anything. I'm by no means perfect... sometimes my outlook on life probably is a fault. I don't see it as a fault to see the best in everyone, every person.

We all have one life, we are all born and we all end up in the same place (belief dependent). I will live my days growing as a person, happy as a father, husband, son, brother, friend, coach, business owner and now... author. I will continue to write every morning. If you want to join me and are active on social media, please add me. If this journey has helped you, speak up and reach out.

It's proof that Building the Chain works. I've written a book in six months on my phone at no cost to my time... proof you can succeed with linking consistency and accountability. What I'm most excited about is the development of myself that this book has allowed me. I've learnt more in six months than ever before, and I have had the amazing opportunity to share it in an individual and crazy way... using this journey and my ADHD to my advantage.

They say strength is never a weakness, but I also believe that every weakness is an opportunity for massive growth. See the world differently, believe in yourself...

- Always Improve
- Always Evolve
- Never Give Up

OC

ABOUT THE AUTHOR

Ollie Campbell is a student of fitness, a sportsman, an entrepreneur, a husband and a father with over 10 years of dedicated education and learning in all realms of fitness and nutrition. He has learnt from some of the greatest minds in health, strength and conditioning, and fitness for the general population.

Having launched the flagship gym Priority 6, with a wide variety of members, his wife and his business partner Simon, Ollie came to the conclusion that mindset was the key to unlocking people's potential. This led to the development of the Build the Chain concept, one of support and day-to-day living.